Date Due

Jun 17 '63			

PRINTED IN U. S. A.

across the water

also by

MICHAEL CAMPBELL

peter perry

across
the water

michael
campbell

the orion press
new york

to ian and jennifer

part | *one*

chapter one

On a brilliant blue morning in October, with the trees partly yellow and brown, the grass shiny with dew, and the air marvellous for the lungs, Kathleen Doyle emerged through the rear hall-door, stood out on top of the stone steps, paused to contemplate the scenery, and thought for a moment that she might burst.

She was now only occasionally homesick for Tipperary and Kilsheelan. A half-hour by bus to the cinemas did not seem to her outrageous: and she loved the country. She was different from the six maids who had preceded her within six months, including her own sister, Finola. To most of them the words of Julia Byrne, the cook, had accurately applied: 'Once they hear the cows mooin', they're off.'

Wearing the pre-breakfast white coat with which Mrs Neelan had equipped her, she was standing on steps that had previously descended to an old farmyard. But Mr Neelan had removed it and put down paving-stones and a small swimming-pool. At the end was the old pink barn from whose roof he had banished the moss. Farther away was the tennis-court with dew-drops glittering on its wire netting this morning, and then green hills and the curving skyline of the Dublin mountains. She had an inclination to begin stamping her feet, as she had seen the Spanish dancers doing that night at the Olympia, clicking her fingers, pushing out her bottom and jerking it sharply up and down.

A pink wing, however, ran back from the pink house, joining up with the barn, and from behind the muslin curtains of the lower kitchen-windows of this wing Julia Byrne frequently inspected the world to see that it was still all right. Kathleen therefore put her hands quietly on her hips and gazed down the drive in search of the postman, her face rosy from twenty-five years in Kilsheelan, her bright eyes behind glasses disguising her almost vacant mind.

There was no sign of him, and she felt suddenly more interested in a vast plate of bacon and eggs and a cup of tea the size of a beer-barrel. Then Richard appeared.

He came round the end of the barn on the grass terrace above the tennis-court, his head down and working from side to side on the autumn morning smells. He was named Richard by Miss Ann, the daughter of the house, after the song, 'Open the Door, Richard'. He never liked to stay in one room for long, and Mrs Neelan did not like his insistent scratching at all.

'Richard!' she shouted, suddenly oblivious of Mrs Neelan sleeping above. The collie stopped. He saw her with obvious pleasure and avoiding the empty swimming-pool came rushing up the steps. She embraced his cool brown and white fur, and sat down on the low stone parapet at one side, which for an instant was like sitting on a block of ice.

'Richard,' she said, into the bony white interior of one ear, 'you're beautiful.'

He averted his brown eyes in embarrassment, but panted with pleasure.

'Richard,' she whispered, 'wait till I tell you. Paddy's taking me to the Manhattan Ballroom tonight.'

He seemed delighted. She at once wanted to explain that soon she would marry Paddy, run a small house, hens, pigs and indeed children with furious energy and never a murmur out of her ever after; and it was tremendous luck because he was much too good-looking for her. Instead she said: 'Let's go and get the mistress's tea.'

She stepped into the hall and tiptoed across the Persian carpet so as not to harm it. Striding down the several stairs into the wing, she flung open the door of the kitchen and entered, with Richard at her heels, crying:

'It's a *glorious* morning!'

Kathleen clapped a hand over her mouth, her eyes open wide with fright. From behind the nearer of the two white bedroom doors came the low, awe-inspiring murmur of Julia Byrne engaged upon the rosary.

'Ssh, Richard,' she said to the dog, who was swiftly circling the modernised kitchen, his claws making a faint clicking on the red flags. 'Ssh,' she repeated, but more to herself this time. She went over to the kettle, her heart racing at the thought of what Julia Byrne might have to say. Kathleen had only been employed for three weeks, and though the cook had twice brought her to tears she was still not sure how inferior her position was supposed to be. The kettle stood steaming on the electric cooker which Mr Neelan had substituted for an old-fashioned range. She wondered if she should lift it, when a voice said:

'Was that *you* bawlin' between me and my devotions?'

Julia Byrne stood in the doorway, dressed in black with the Sacred Heart in a large brooch at the centre of her chest. She had a square head, like a man's, with strong grey hair standing up. She was a Pioneer, and two of her six brothers were priests.

'Gosh, I'm terribly sorry,' said Kathleen, 'I thought you were done long ago.'

'It's not *me* you need apologise to, Kathleen Doyle. God will recompense you, have no fear. I've warned you before. You're steeped in sin, like others I could name. What are you doing?'

'I thought I'd make the tea.'

'*Give* me that,' said Julia, stepping across, jabbing Kathleen with a sharp black elbow and pulling the kettle away.

There was such fury in this movement that Kathleen fell back in amazement and fright. She went to the window and looked blankly through the muslin curtains at the brown leaves in the empty pool, feeling tears on the way and concentrating hard on the Manhattan Ballroom.

'There's no morals at all in the country,' said Julia Byrne.

'You're all pigs, like the ones in the back that Himself is so fond of. Disgusting. The devil has got into that Tom Neelan. Reading dirty books about animals till all hours. Herself was on the phone to that Charlie Gerraty last night. Did you know that? As for Miss Ann and her so-called fiancy! Things were very different in Shrewsbury Road, I can tell you. That was a decent town house.'

Having heard this incomprehensible speech, Kathleen turned and saw that Mrs Neelan's tea was ready and Julia was engaged upon the breakfast. Richard lay on the floor, watching and waiting for her. She took the cup and left the kitchen, and he followed.

Mrs Moira Neelan had the room above the other hall-door, at the front. On moving here from Shrewsbury Road six months before, she and her husband had agreed on separate bedrooms partly because Tom was determined on reading books by Dr Heinrich Stumpff on the pig industry through half the night. Her room overlooked the gravel sweep of the drive, then a hedge, then green fields, the roof of the Murrough-Bryants' house set among trees, the city far off, Dublin Bay, and the sea leading away towards the world.

It was what they called a wonderful view, but after six months she was sick of it. The only consolation was that it was seen with the greatest difficulty, through a semi-circular window at waist-level. This she considered the silliest window ever invented, but Cyril Hampton, an English Catholic who had come to star in the pre-London production of *Death by Proxy* and had been invited out by her before anyone else could do so, had assured her that it was a perfect example of the Georgian complex about fans.

Asleep under her white satin bedspread, a small woman with fluffy blonde hair spread out on the pillow, she was dreaming.

She stood at the top of the sairs in the hall of the President's house, radiant in white satin. Tom was at her side, looking small and stocky but important. He could do that at times; especially now, with the President's badge of office on a blue ribbon across his evening dress. A string band somewhere was playing a selection from *My Fair Lady,* and mounting the stairway from below, two by two, came Dublin.

She could see the line winding away through the hall, in evening gowns and white ties and tails. Only a few young people had been asked, and she greeted them without a word; merely a handshake and an inclination of the head. But many of the wives had been with her at the Loreto Convent School, worked with her in the Red Cross, played bridge with her, and, in a few cases, drunk with her in the Hibernian and the Shelbourne and to these she spoke briefly: 'How nice to see you, Shelah'—conscious of the poor dear's sudden sense of inferiority, but without going too far to help. Then, as the wife moved on to Tom, she turned to the husband and said, 'Rory, how nice! And how's business? Flourishing, I suppose?'—knowing well that compared with her own husband's achievement business was at a full stop.

The diplomatic corps, however, was of more account. (The priesthood, she was aware, even in her dream, she had received on the previous evening. She had always shown a flair—and was now extremely intimate with the Papal Nuncio. Up the stairs they came, sleek, cultivated gentlemen—except for Sir Ronald Higginbottom—dangling with ribbons and medals and greying over the ears. The French ambassador bent and kissed her hand, and she tossed her blonde head and stole a glance at his wife's black bun. His chargé d'affaires followed, with some young beauty to whom he was oblivious already as the First Lady said: 'Why, Jean-Pierre!' and shot an amused glance into his Gallic eyes. Then Ann approached, causing some confusion in her mind because she ought perhaps to have been receiving. But in that she could only have played a very humble part. She did look sweet, poor lamb; so pretty, with a sufficient share of her mother's looks. She had not, unfortunately, inherited that sparkle. Yet there were men who liked a quiet demeanour. For example, young Brendan Smith, who was with her, a nice-looking boy, rather gauche but very satisfactory, being the elder son of the Attorney-General, who was a notoriously good Catholic with the minimum of political affiliation—which was important to Tom in his position. She let them pass, and then, for all her poise, her heart stopped.

Charlie Gerraty was approaching. He was four couples away, but she scarcely noticed the others. He looked more diplomatic than the whole corps put together, in spite of being an architect; tall, with wavy black hair above his handsome, lined face. Tonight, indeed, he was unbelievably handsome. She barely observed his wife, Norah, her old school friend who stood beside him, pitifully unaware of the rôle she was called upon to play. When he came near his smiling eyes looked straight through her to the Reality, yet with adoration. 'Congratulations,' he said softly and with infinite meaning. 'Thank you,' she said, returning it in full. Suddenly he kissed her hand in a way that outdid the whole corps, scarcely bending at all but raising it up to his face. It seemed most excessive for one who had presented no credentials and was Dublin-born, and when it was over she glanced at Tom out of the corner of her eye, but he was too busy flattering poor Norah.

And then the dream swung away in a breathlessly exciting manner, and she was in an upstairs chamber, with the distant sound of the ball proceeding somewhere below, and Charlie had appeared under one of the wings of the four-poster on which she lay, and was bending over her, his eyes half-closed. She put her hands up and clenched her fingers tight into his strong wiry black hair, and his face came slowly closer, in an ecstasy of passion, and then was upon her, with a wet splashing all over her cheeks and fur enveloping her so that she fought wildly for breath, and struck out, with a piercing scream.

'Richard!' cried Kathleen, aghast, and nearly dropping the teacup.

chapter two

'Oh, my God,' said Grania Agerton-Willy. She had divorced Antony of that name in the spring; and ten years previously Reggie Price-Jones to whom she had first surrendered the treasured Murrough-Bryant. In her rare black moments life seemed to be a series of hyphens.

'Is it too bright, madam? Amn't I a thoughtless silly?' said Flanagan. He drew the heavy red curtains on one of the two windows again, with long pale hands emerging from the cuffs of his white coat.

The others he left pulled back, so that the old panelled room was still filled with light.

'I feel rather tired this morning, Flanagan.'

They both knew that it was a meaningful admission. She was accustomed to rising in a lively condition, and taking a glass of light champagne at eight a.m. after nights that left her companions moaning and suicidal. But she had only arrived from London by plane the previous evening and, emotionally and physically, it had been a strain. Even if André had not departed with Sandra Bell, returning to her father and to Edenmore and its atmosphere and memories, was always thus. So this morning the lines under her blue eyes, in her remarkably young face, were very apparent, and her celebrated long black hair, parted down the centre, did not look well.

'If I may say so, I'm not surprised, madam. You don't spare yourself, you really don't. Your vitality is quite fantastic to a frail thing like me. Lord save us, I'd be a wreck so I would.'

She was grateful, as ever, for this amazingly tactful description of a broken romance and flight home. Perhaps it was truer than the truth.

They were both the product of two cultures. In him it was expressed in his speech. It had intrigued her from the first. He was at that time—seven years before—employed by the Terenures, who were paying him a pittance. Within weeks he had joined her and Tony, then temporarily resident with her father at Edenmore. Most usefully, Lord Terenure had taught him to drive a car, so that he could be both butler and chauffeur at a criminal wage. Surprisingly, he not only understood the engine but treated it with a surgeon's hands; likewise electrical fittings and other mysteries. Tony had left her Flanagan, the Bentley, and the alimony. She remembered how sitting in the back beside André a month ago, with Flanagan taking them to Cannes, the Count had called him with hidden mockery 'your Celtic treasure' and Flanagan's neck had blushed. He came from Cahirciveen, and was proud of it.

He did not look as frail as he had said. In his white coat and black trousers he looked well built. He was forty-nine, like herself, but his agility, his lively eyes, mobile hands, and ready smile so rare in a butler, were youthful. At the same time his square, freckled face was old maidish; the front of his wavy, auburn hair was a most ingenious toupé; and even his smile might be considered a deception, since the top row was false.

'Perhaps a wreck is what I am, Flanagan,' she said.

'Indeed you're not!' he exclaimed. 'Madam is a picture. But sure you'll think it's me and my blarney,' he added, moving suddenly to the fireplace and starting to shovel the ashes into a bucket. 'I don't know how it is, but as soon as we're back in this fantastic little land of ours, I'm always the same. Blathering.'

He neatly swept the grate.

'That's all right. I understand. I'm Irish too, you know.'

'Indeed I do, madam, but somehow I always forget, heaven help me. Madam seems so civilised,' he said, standing before the mantelpiece and uttering the last word in an Oxford accent. 'And that low, heavenly voice, with none of that jumpin' and jivin'.'

'Thank you, Flanagan, but I'm not sure that I should be pleased.'

It had sounded like an uncharacteristic betrayal of Cahirciveen and the voices of the West. He was an untiring support to her, but sometimes he went far enough to make her feel guilty.

'Oh, madam preserves the better part of her origins, I know that—a sense of humour quite beyond the Saxon, and an interest in all sorts. Indeed, the most catholic taste in companions, so contrary to the rather stubborn exclusiveness of English society. Honest to God, they talk about democracy,' he said, his face suddenly lighting up with the conception. 'Sure, *we're* the democrats!' He raised a hand in triumph. 'But there I go again, God help me. Your post, madam.'

Flanagan handed her a silver tray, on which were two letters.

She sat up higher in the bed. Her clothing contrasted brilliantly with her black hair. Over her slim girlish figure she wore pyjamas with a pattern of scarlet patches on a black ground, which had been designed for her by Anatole Robbeck who had since vanished with the Duke of Shropshire's younger daughter. She picked up a gold paper-knife from the bedside table, and hoped she knew who they were from.

She had written in advance from S.W.1. It always happened; even this time, following an emotional crisis. All at once, at the prospect of returning, the outer 'civilised' world was empty of living beings. Individuals did not exist. There was no time, energy, or even capacity left for thought, conversation, personal relations or affections. That charming person, Henry Moore, who had come to her last cocktail-party in the Knightsbridge flat, had quite summed it up with his Man, Woman, and Child, full-stop; and Picasso had shown truthfully that you could put the subject's eyes coming out of her nostrils without suffering much individual loss. So she found herself dropping off postcards in advance to real people still clinging to an island in the Atlantic, informing them of her return: to Martin O'Keeffe, who had made off with one of her mother's paintings by A.E., of a fairy in a bog, and had admitted it to her in an exuberant and flattering poem; to Dermot Sleator, who had pushed an eminent London art critic out of one of the upper windows; to Terence Keogh, who had driven someone else's station-wagon clean through the marquee at her last Horse Show dance, on the supposition that his wife was inside.

But the letters were from none of these; which was satisfying and characteristic. One was from Lavinia Westmacott who was having a few people to dinner at her place in Kildare. The other was from Antoinette Haslipp who was giving a dance in Galway. She glanced at Flanagan, who was pretending to be occupied with the fireplace, and thought how right he was about 'all sorts'. She had only now recalled, with sudden alarm, that Hilda Manningham was coming over with Patrick, at her invitation. It was an act of sympathy. Reggie Manningham had disappeared to Jamaica with the deb of the year. It was also partly, since Hilda was not a particular friend, because Edenmore was so perfect that she liked to share it. Her father, somehow, did not.

'Master Patrick is arriving on the three o'clock plane, Flanagan,' she said. 'And I think I'll lunch in town before that. I hope you hadn't forgotten?'

'I had not, madam. I've been out there putting a shine on the Bentley that would blind you for the past hour.'

There was no reason for her to go, and certainly not to lunch, but she was not ready for a solitary session with her aged father. She picked up a silver comb and began to improve her long black hair. She shared it with her sister, Delia. They had been the lovely 'Murrough-Bryant girls', reputed by malicious Dublin report to come of a long line of gypsies. Delia, too, had lost a brace of husbands, through living too well, and retained nothing—nothing human. She, Grania, had been presented with Patrick by Price-Jones, and the son was agreeably unlike his father. Her own father had christened his daughters in his 'Irish' phase, and their surnames had never matched, even from the start.

'It's been on my conscience, Flanagan,' she said. 'When you met me at the airport yesterday I was too exhausted to ask you about your own journey the night before.'

'Ah well, madam,' he smiled rather sadly, 'the boat jumped about like blue murder, and I wasn't feeling too well. A priest talked to me all the way, and honest to God I could have killed him.'

'I'm afraid being in service to a Black Protestant has done you no good.'

'Ah not at all, madam, not at all. Don't blame yourself. I'd lapsed before. Anyway, driving the Bentley to and from the ship was great. I liked that. We had style.'

'And how are things below?'

'Oh well. Well. Miss Doyle has her airs and graces, of course, but she's a pretty thing and what else would you expect? As for Mary Cullen, well, you know her, milady. She cooks a good roast.'

'Yes.'

She had come over for the Horse Show, and found her father maidless, but also found that their comparatively new neighbours, the Neelans, were rumoured to be well suited. Within days Finola Doyle had left them and come to Edenmore at a higher wage. How this was viewed she neither knew nor cared. She had not met the neighbours. Patrick only had run across, or rather stumbled into, Mr Neelan in the bar at the Louth Hunt Ball and described him as a screaming bore.

'Well, now, the question is,' said Flanagan, rubbing his long white hands together, 'is it to be a glass of Heidsieck or a cup of tea?'

'I don't seem to be in the mood for champagne. It had better be tea.'

'And toast perhaps?'

'Yes, toast.'

'I'll tell Finola to bring it right away, madam,' said Flanagan with sudden formality; and he backed out of the room.

She looked at her gold watch on the table. It was ten—hours later than her usual time. But she had told him to call her late.

Her eyes took in the old oak panels with their not very feminine prints. It was her father's home. Her mother had been too preoccupied to change it, and the daughters had married too early. 'I'm back,' she thought, 'I'm home again.'

She had not properly taken it in this morning, though the previous evening it had been different. She had stood in this room and looked out at the twilight and been filled with emotion and a sense of shame at having lived away as she had lived. She felt suddenly a completely different—a very simple and innocent —person. Away in the silence they might have been cutting down the cherry orchard. Fortunately there was none, and they were not. But she had thought 'My youth, my happiness' and remembered her mother, and wondered what she would have thought of her two daughters now. It was not necessarily part of her self-criticism. It was a completely open question. She had no idea of the answer. Her mother had belonged to her father's 'Irish' phase too. She was dark and beautiful. She played the harp in a special costume, intoning Celtic verse. She was one of those who had fought the cultural rebellion rather than the other, and when with Yeats she found that a terrible beauty had not been born she took to sherry, and ultimately died of it, unsettling her daughters for ever in the process. At the same time they were like her: she, too, had appreciated artists, and received them in this very room with a bottle beside her bed.

Time had wrought strange and alarming effects. In three months she would be fifty and she found it very difficult to believe.

But life was tempting, and so was the sunshine, and without a moment's further reflection she stepped out of bed, and slim and young in Anatole Robbeck's scarlet patches she went to the window with the curtains pulled back and looked out.

The vista of the tennis-court, the great trees and high wall and the mountains beyond, was stirring and new every time. But her gaze was held by one figure in it. Because it was a Saturday, her father, Major Murrough-Bryant, who still went to work in town, was seated on the court on a small wooden stool which his brother had sent him one Christmas from Kenya, where it had been carved by one of his boys, or bearers, or whatever they were called. This was his invariable recreation, frequently in teeming rain, though it was seldom that anyone played on his immaculate court. Wearing a shabby sports coat and corduroy trousers, he bent over and inserted a tool of some kind into the grass and pulled up almost invisible weeds by the hour—indeed by the day. She examined his straight back and tried to comprehend that in spite of his age, and his apartness, and his enduringly strange military title, he had once held her on his knee, kissed her good-night, taken her to the zoo and led her to the altar. But the personal connection escaped her, and gave way to the abstract but fervent hope that her own existence would not be reduced in the end to plucking dandelions from their muddy bed.

chapter three

As she was passing the gates of Edenmore, Moira Neelan's ten-horse-power car backfired with a terrific bang. She uttered a brief cry of astonishment and fear, and the car sped away on its own towards the opposite hedge. She began to wrestle with it, and to her surprise succeeded. There was a scraping of brambles and ripe blackberries nodded at her through the window, but she steered it round and recaptured the centre of the road.

For some moments, as she continued in the sunshine and still-ness, it seemed like a just retribution: she had turned her head away at the time, and was trying to see down the drive past the rhododendron bushes. But then she smiled; for the car had a personality and it had expressed her own feelings about them almost exactly. They were settlers, foreigners and Protestant heathen, without morals. She knew them well, though she had never met them.

To her left, beyond the hedges among the fields, the smoke of chimneys and bonfires went straight up in thin pillars. To her right a high wall insisted on the position of Major Murrough-Bryant as a landowner, and, like the thick wet rhododendrons, protected Edenmore from rude noises. Above the wall were brown beeches around which the rooks were still wheeling and cawing as a result of the explosion. The entire scene was an irri-tation; not least in that it was so undeniably Edenmore and she had difficulty in even remembering the name of her own house, which was Hill View.

However, the irritation passed and, driving confidently again, she examined herself in the mirror and decided at once that she was chic, attractive and experienced; just the right age. The little beige hat, with a veil, newly bought at Slyne's, was a complete success, and the matching beige suit from Sybil Connolly had already proved itself in the Irish wars. Since Tom had forced her into exile, going into town was like riding into battle. It had become an event: today, indeed, more than ever before.

Charlie Gerraty had phoned Tom last night, unaware that he was in London and was not flying home until this afternoon. Julia Byrne had handed her the phone with one of her looks, and she had found great difficulty in speaking. It had developed into an invitation to meet Charlie and Norah for a drink and lunch. They were just back from Cannes.

Now, as the wall ended—exactly as the wall ended—the new houses began. They were Tom's. But she had the feeling that they were also hers, in the rôle of patroness; on behalf of the wives, as it were, and their kitchens and nurseries and so on; all that really made a house. She would call some day and surprise them.

The houses continued for quite some time. A notice-board still advertised them at £2,750 each, but they had gone, she knew, within weeks; a whole village of them, with new white cul-de-sacs running among them. They were all the same, in bright red brick, semi-detached, with bow-windows; most harmonious. She would have liked one herself, but for the neighbours.

It was satisfying but still a little strange to be set apart as one of the Establishment. Only a week ago her wedding anniversary had recalled that she had met Tom Neelan twenty-three years before at a hop in the Anglesea Tennis Club. She was the prettiest member and very quick at the net. She was also secretary to the manager of a Munster and Leinster bank, and he was travelling in typewriters and a terrible talker even then. She had won him at once, and his words, with their hints of ambition, had reduced her to submission after several weeks.

The swelling capital had begun. She was among new shops and pubs, and a vast new red brick Catholic church, and traffic, and she had to concentrate. When Tom had first bought her this car—because in the mountains she might as well give up without it—it had been unmanageable for several weeks whenever there were any other cars about. In Moore Street she had gripped the gear-lever, which was oddly placed on the steering-wheel, and put it into first, and for some reason gone backwards very fast into a fruit-stall, tumbling it over the elderly woman behind who had been bawling out her wares in a lusty and confident manner and was instantly reduced to complete silence. It had cost her the contents of her handbag to keep it out of the Dublin papers.

Now she was managing well. She understood and liked the car's personality. In Tom's Jaguar she never felt at ease. She was confident, and suddenly for the first time in her life decided to pass the car in front. She released the indicator, and edged her machine out, tense and excited. There was the sudden brief blast of a klaxon from behind. She flung out her foot at the brake, and before she could recover she saw dimly a vast Bentley with a chauffeur in front and a woman in the back, gliding by, as if on air, and disappearing into the traffic ahead.

She knew this car. It belonged to the neighbours, or more specifically to a loose-living notorious b. who was the biggest servant-stealer in the country.

For a while her thoughts were such a confusion of hatred, anger and outrage that before she realised it she was in Harcourt Street, part of the old city which Tom was keen to rebuild, and then in Stephen's Green, where he wanted to erect a multi-storeyed garage for parking.

Parking was indeed her problem now, and she decided to risk the Royal Irish Automobile Club being full. As she turned into Dawson Street she saw that it was not. (They put a sign out.) Driving off the street, under the archway into the garage, she hoped that the Bentley and its occupants were not here. Not only was it still 'Royal' but it was one of the few places left for a certain type; and, sure enough, although there were no Mur-rough-Bryants there were two examples walking out; elderly, a man and woman, both in tweeds, talking in that 'haw-haw' way that made one want to ask who the devil did they think they *were* any more. 'Backaway, backaway,' said the attendant, and she managed it well. He knew her and looked surprised.

Walking down Dawson Street, she should have felt happy. The sun was really warm now. 'Town' was full of Saturday-morning life and excitement. There were geraniums on the Mansion House. She saw Harry Murphy chatting with the Callinans on the corner of Anne Street, and Betty Farren going into the Cottage Industries Shop. But there were suddenly butterflies darting about inside her.

Dublin was odd. You saw someone about for years and years, and they were nothing. Then you did the rumba with them, and talked a little more than usual with them at the annual dinner and dance of Contemporary Tweed Incorporated and suddenly they were in your dreams, playing a rôle that it was difficult to overlook. The dance had been held a month ago, and she had thought that the immediate departure of the Gerratys to Cannes would dispel its effects. It had not been so.

She descended the steps on legs of string and opened the glass door, and there was Norah seated on the tartan couch, tall, dark, and slightly alarming.

'Moira dear, how nice to see you,' she said.

It was only twelve o'clock. There were two men at the bar, talking to George, and neither was Charlie.

'Hallo there. Gosh, Norah, you're lookin' great.'

She was decidedly brown.

Moira moved in beside her, taking off her beige driving gloves and laying them on the table. Her hands were trembling a little.

'When did you get back? I'm sure you had a gorgeous time. I can't *tell* you . . .'

The waiter was upon her.

'I'll have a dry sherry. Will you have another of those? Ah go on, you may as well.' (It was gin and French, and Norah accepted.) 'I can't *tell* you, Norah, how I envy you. If you only knew.'

'Really?'

'If you *only* knew. God, you've got a great tan!'

This old friend had always slightly put her out, always at first meeting, at least. She had a way of warming up and becoming lively, and had a well-known effect on men. But her more usual mood was detached, and perhaps even superior. That was how she had been at Loreto, when they were at school together. She had grown into a woman who for some reason was handsome, even though she had a long nose and eyes too close together. She was always smart; and today she was wearing a green dress of some silky, shiny material, with lapels, on one of which was a large piece of gold jewellery.

'You're looking well yourself,' she said. 'I like the hat.'

'Do you honestly? Slyne's. Do you think it's becoming?'

Moira turned and checked on it again, in the mirror behind them, straightening it a little. The veil was tickling her forehead, and obscured the view with a collection of black spots which were doubly confusing in the mirror, but it was worth it.

'It's *most* becoming,' said Norah.

'Tom'll probably have a fit. I'm meeting him at the airport at three. I expect Charlie told you. One of his business jaunts. He goes over quite often now.'

The waiter brought the drinks. Moira paid him, sipped hers, and said, with an effort,

'Is Charlie coming?'

'Oh, he is indeed,' Norah answered, in a tone which Moira termed to herself 'sarcastic' and unsuited to so lucky a wife.

'Tell me all about Cannes. I suppose you'd marvellous weather even at this time of year?'

'Wonderful. Wonderful. I could've settled there for good.'

'You don't tell me! And did Charlie enjoy himself, or need I ask?'

'He did indeed. He went casino-mad, the poor man. I thought we'd have to sell the car and all we possessed.'

'You don't say!'

Moira was aware of a strange relief that it was only the casino.

'Ah, well,' she added. 'These architects can well afford it. I know all about it from Tom.'

Norah smiled, and said nothing.

'Of course,' Norah remarked, after a pause, 'there was a crowd of us, you know.'

'So I heard. Ah, you'd want an Irish crowd to have some sport.'

'The Callinans . . .'

'I just saw them outside in the street.'

'The Brophys. David Keely, James Larkin and Kevin Barry. Three bachelor architects let loose on the Riviera! Of course they spent the whole time in the bar.'

'You don't say! Tch, tch. Typical, I suppose. Honest to God, Norah, you make me feel like Cinderella or something. I think I'll have another of these, won't you? Ah, you may as well. It's not often I get the chance to enjoy myself these days.'

They ordered.

'I heard you were prospering,' said Norah, in her mischievous and rather frightening tone of voice. 'Charlie said Tom was building all over the place.'

Tom had employed a less expensive architect. She wondered if Norah 'meant' something, but decided that it was just her manner of speaking.

'It's all right for him, Norah,' she said. 'He's in every day. *I'm* stuck out in the mountains. I'm sure I'm going to be frozen stiff this winter in that mausoleum.'

'Now Moira! It's Georgian and . . .'

'I don't care if it's Greek. There's not a soul in sight. Except that benighted village, and those Murrough-Bryants below.'

'She was at Cannes with a black man, gambling fit to bust. I mean Agerton-Willy or whatever she calls herself.'

'God!'

'I was just having my hair done in Jules and I saw them again in an old *Tatler*. Well, he's not really black, but near enough. Count André Risky or something.'

'My God.'

'There was a good one of you at the races.'

'In the *Tatler?*'

'No, I think it was the *Irish Tatler and Sketch*. The new one.'

'Oh. We didn't get our copy yet. The post takes all day to arrive. There's an old wretch on a bicycle and the hills are terrible.'

The place was filling up now. Conversation was loud. There were several familiar faces, but none of them important.

Norah took a gold holder out of her green handbag and placed a cork-tipped cigarette in it. She lit it with a gold lighter. They had both been smoking freely, she with long, thoughtful draughts, Moira with light, heedless puffs.

'Did she ask you to her Horse Show dance? You were neighbours then, weren't you?'

'We were,' replied Moira. 'And she did not. She stole Finola Doyle, that's all.'

'I heard it was a riot.'

'Oh, I've no doubt! You know, of course, that that woman has stolen every servant in Dublin in her time; not that they last long with her. In any case Agerton-Willy isn't even there. It's just the old boy.'

'I think he's sweet,' said Norah.

'He's what? What did you say?'

'Sweet. He has such a charming and courtly way with the ladies, the old flatterer.'

Moira was astonished; but then it seemed to her natural that Norah should know him and she should not. Whatever the reason for this, it was disturbing.

'Nevertheless, Norah, you can't get away from the fact that he supports her carryings on. Just listen to me. I've had six maids in as many months. Three of them said the cinemas were too far away. Two of them became pregnant, and Julia Byrne spotted it at once each time and they left on the Holyhead boat.

(The cranky old thing, I don't know what I'd do without her. She's been with me twenty years, you know.) Well, anyway, in between I had Finola Doyle. Being from the wilds of Tipperary she seemed content enough, and being such a flirt and so full of herself she seemed safe from anything serious. So back comes her ladyship from one of her little excursions, hears the good news, gets through to Finola behind my back, offers her the world, and away she goes. Now I've got her scatter-brained sister, Kathleen. Oh, I'd like to get my hands on Mrs Agerton-Willy!'

Norah laughed, in her quiet way.

'Then of course Tom meets the son in the bar at the Louth Hunt Ball, and being Tom, and hail fellow well met and all that, and between you and me being a fool about people who are supposed to be what he calls well-educated, especially when he's had a few, he makes great pals with him, so it seems. The funny thing is,' Moira laughed too, 'Tom could've told him something that would have taken the wind out of his sails!'

'You interest me.'

'I was sworn not to say a thing about it. But I'll tell you this. That family's due for a shock!'

'Really?'

'If all goes well.'

Norah observed her friend, smoking the while.

'Tom's becoming a man of power,' she said.

'Well, honestly, Norah . . .' Moira put a hand on Norah's shiny green arm. She felt elated, and almost ready to confide everything. 'He must be a very different person when he's at work.'

She giggled.

'They all are,' said Norah, 'I've often wished I was a secretary.'

'But you were.'

There was a pause.

'So I was. So I was. And so were you.'

'Happy days,' said Moira, unaware of hostility.

'Well,' said Norah, after a while, 'I can't say I've had any trouble in the new place. You must come and see it. I think we'll be having a house-warming next month.'

'Oh I'd love to, Norah.'

'Alfredo's the perfect butler and Angelina's a wonderful cook.'

'My God! Do you mean to say you've two Italians?'

'Oh yes. They're a pair of darlings. Besides, we wanted to make a complete change from that dreary place at Foxrock. Charlie designed it, with ideas he picked up in Helsinki when he stayed with Jolainin, and I did all the décor. We're not so far from you. Just across the mountains. We've a wonderful view of the sea and Bray Hotel, and the Sugarloaf mountains. Charlie believes very strongly in windows.'

'Well!'

'We've nothing like your land, of course. How's Tom's farming?'

'Oh . . . oh, well, he reads books, and Paddy, the lad from the village, does the work. It's a wild notion at his time of life.'

This was wrong, Moira thought, as soon as she had said it. She had made enough surrenders.

'But, to be fair,' she added, 'Tom has his head screwed on. Did you know he gave a speech, while you were away, on agriculture, emigration, keeping in touch with the land and God knows what to the Rathmines Technical Students?'

'I did not.'

'Of course, coming from a business man—and building homes for agricultural workers from the West at that—it was a sensation.'

'I can imagine.'

'Front page in the *Irish Press*. I suppose you didn't know . . . I'm sure I shouldn't be telling you this, Norah . . . Tom's going up for the Senate next time.'

'No!'

'That's right. But not a word. Of course he has "the Irish" very well. I only wish that old man of his had done a bit of fighting, instead of running a typewriter shop.'

'I know. Give me France, any day.'

'Ah France! Give me Ireland, that's what I say.'

But someone was leaning towards her. She had almost forgotten and her heart leaped. He was tall and dark, with pale blue eyes. He spoke, and his words were rich and eloquent.

'How's the form?' he said.

chapter four

Hilda Manningham and Patrick Price-Jones were seated in a taxi in Knightsbridge. He had a hangover, and she looked depressed. He assumed that her set face and silent manner were explained by her husband's disappearance with another to Jamaica, of which his mother had informed him. It was an aristocratic face with strong cheek-bones and chin, heavily made up today about the eyes. She appeared to be wearing diamond ear-rings, and was indeed extremely well-dressed for Ireland, with a short mink jacket over a black dress.

He himself had put on country clothes for Ireland. They were smart too. They included a brown check sports coat, cavalry twill trousers and suede shoes. He had been to Oxford. He was tall and good-looking, with a plentiful inheritance of his mother's black hair. Because he had excelled at English literature, Oxford had led him to an advertising agency, and he had suddenly decided that he could endure it no longer. He had a hangover, because the previous night the office had given him a farewell party. They had all joined in vilifying their employers and their employment, and Patrick had ended the evening in the arms of June, one of the executive's secretaries. He wished now that he had been able to travel a day earlier with his mother, who had left to prepare Edenmore and her father to receive Hilda Manningham. He was going there to think; because everything at the moment was very confusing.

Patrick was looking with disinterest at the women streaming in and out of the shops. A newspaper-seller was shouting something unintelligible beside posters saying, 'Self-Government Clashes', 'Bank Manager Shot', and 'Film Star Coshed'. In a few hours, he thought, it would all be forgotten. They were travelling away to the green and quiet.

Hilda Manningham appeared to share this notion, for the sole remark she made before they arrived at the Cromwell Road air terminal was, 'Oh dear, I *am* so looking forward to being in Ireland. My friends who've been to the Horse Show tell me it's perfect heaven.'

'Yes, it's rather fun,' he said, and was conscious of slipping into Hilda's language.

She did not speak again, and in his condition he decided that she was going to be an excellent companion. It would be a peaceful journey.

When they had handed over their luggage, which consisted of one suitcase of his and three belonging to Hilda, she went to buy a copy of *Vogue* and he stood beside her, and a voice behind him said:

'Be the holy, and by all that's . . . it's not, it is, it's not, it is, it's not, it is!'

Patrick turned.

'Oh hallo,' he said.

It was either that or a cry of despair that would have terrified everyone in the terminal.

Mr Neelan was stocky. He had a very red face with a large ginger moustache, and spoke through a cigarette which was always at one side of his mouth. He wore a belted, ostentatious camel-hair overcoat and a high black hat whose brim almost covered his eyes. It allowed, however, a glimpse of one of his gingery eyebrows because this was screwed down over one eye in a conspiratorial manner, while he cocked his head on one side to give the gesture more emphasis. It also prevented the smoke going into that eye, but the overall effect was of secrecy and private knowledge.

'Be the holy, Patrick,' he repeated. 'This is an historic meeting—a meeting of the minds, as it were. You're *not* going to tell me,' one fist sprang from its overcoat pocket and struck against Patrick's chest, 'that you're on the one-fifty?'

'I am, as a matter of fact.'

Mr Neelan took a pace back, and, oblivious of observers, went through an absurd charade expressive of amazement. His eyes opened wide and the ginger eyebrow disappeared under the brim. His mouth gaped, yet, strangely, without losing the cigarette. He held his arms on high. He was wide open, and Patrick was tempted to take the small black umbrella from Hilda Manningham's arm and spear him in the chest.

'It's the fates,' he said, 'the lares and penates, kismet, Nemesis, and so on, and what have you. As you were!' He held up a hand like a policeman, halting himself. 'Now tell me . . . ahh . . . your bag and baggage, corporeal possessions, effects and impedimenta . . . now where did you . . .?'

'You give your case in over there.'

'Right. Understood. All correct. Now you dig yourself in and don't budge till I'm with you again. These aeronautical displays, traffickings, hither-and-thither and so on and so forth, they upset the old *status quo*. I don't know where I am with all these damn tickets, *billets-doux* . . . My God, what have I done with the bloody things now? Ah, here we are. *Je reviens,* as the Greeks say.'

He picked up a new grey suitcase and hurried away. They watched.

'Well!' said Hilda Manningham. 'Who is that perfectly frightful little man?'

'He's a neighbour of ours,' murmured Patrick.

'And do you mean to say he's going to travel with us?'

'I'm afraid I can't see any way out of it.'

The distant transaction was taking some time. Mr Neelan was holding the responsible official in urgent conversation. Then he returned, inescapably.

'It occurs to me, Patrick,' he said, 'that you have given me due cause to strip you of all honours, orders, decorations, the shield and scutcheon, the star and garter, placing you in the dog-house, serving you from time to time with a bowl of water and a crust, and shunning your company from this out.'

'I'm frightfully sorry. What . . . ?'

'Because you have neglected to introduce me to the charming lady at your side.'

'Oh dear. Of course. Mr Neelan. Mrs Manningham.'

Mr Neelan raised his hat high, revealing ginger hair going straight back over a balding head.

'Well met by moonlight,' he said. 'Or rather I should say, by the terminal, eh, Patrick? *Ad terminum.* Ahh . . . Am I to take it, Mrs Manningham, that we shall be fortunate enough to have you as a *compagnon de voyage?*'

'Yes, actually.'

'Admirable. Admirable. Tell me . . . ahh . . . Patrick, my boy.' Mr Neelan tilted his head and hat to one side, nudged Patrick with an elbow, screwed up one eye, and spoke in a rumbling whisper through the corner of his mouth with the cigarette. 'In honour of camaraderie, *savoir-vivre,* the regiment, and the old *esprit de corps,* and what have you . . .' He threw back his head and spoke normally: 'What about a jar?'

'I don't frankly think we have time. The bus will be leaving any minute now.'

'Right.' Mr Neelan held up his hand. 'Your word is law. No further argument. *Nemine contradicente et modus operandi.* Where is the said omnibus, by the way?'

'It's outside. We may as well go and sit in it now.'

'Accepted. An admirable proposal. By the way, it's within the rules . . . prerogatives . . . ?'

'Oh yes, certainly.'

'In that case let us adjourn without further prevarication. Lead, and we shall follow. The baggage, our impedimenta, is in safe hands, I take it?'

'Yes, yes.'

Patrick had determined to sit beside Hilda, but Mr Neelan gripped his arm as he was climbing into the bus, and said:

'You sit with me and let us enjoy the community of similar minds.'

They sat opposite Hilda, and Mr Neelan bent his head towards Patrick and said, in the same rumbling and secret manner:

'Well, well, well, very charming, very *élégante* as they say, not a widow, I trust? . . . I note the funereal garb . . . come on, put me right, put me right.'

'No, no. Her husband's away in Jamaica.'

'You don't tell me!'

'I do.'

'Oh, very nice too, very nice indeed. The old *soleil,* you know. But I presume, without his charming lady, it must be business as usual?'

'I gather he's busy.'

'Jamaica where labour itself is pleasure, eh? *Labor ipse voluptas.*'

'Yes.'

People began getting into the bus, and Patrick's attention wandered. He was thinking that still worse encounters might be possible. He had just decided that he knew no one when large steel pincers appeared to settle around his left elbow and squeeze tight, so that he had to restrain himself from crying.

' . . . the advantages of culture, though *I* was not at Oxford. But between the *via media* and the ultimate *you* know, as well as *I* know, Patrick, that it's a matter of . . . stop! . . . wait now, wait now, what's the word I want, the *mot propre,* the *mot juste,* the ahhh . . . come on, come on, don't fail me now . . . put me right . . . let's have the benefit of your ahh.'

The pincer-grip squeezed and relaxed, squeezed and relaxed, affectionately.

'I'm afraid I didn't quite . . .'

'Intuition! That's it. Intuition. Feminine, male, neuter, whatever you like. We're not concerned with that for the moment.'

Mr Neelan was still talking as the bus moved away, through unknown streets. He was leaning very close, the brim of his hat almost rubbing Patrick's cheek. The cigarette came out on Patrick's side, under the ginger moustache, and as Mr Neelan spoke it shed a light shower of ash on his cavalry twill trousers. He brushed it off with a discreet and regular movement. Mr Neelan's left hand, crossed over for the purpose, lay on his elbow, and as his attention wandered Mr Neelan, less through awareness it would appear than a kind of spontaneous action, brought the pincer-grip to bear without warning.

'Of course it was a case of the old folly de grandeur, but all the same ahh . . . you can't help, you know what I mean? . . . The man had his own persona—non gratis or whatever you like to call it. D'you see?'

'I didn't exactly . . .'

'Well, between the *via media* and the ultimate each of us has his own particular individual, ahhh . . . and I'd be the last to . . .'

When the factory buildings began, and continued to go past, one after another, Patrick, with his brain spinning, found that he was asking himself persistently what *could* possibly come between the *via media* and the ultimate, though he knew that the question was senseless.

Then fields appeared, and a plane was taking off into the blue, and it was the airport.

As soon as they arrived Patrick, without a word, went to the lavatory to recover his wits.

Mr Neelan appeared in the place beside him. 'Ahh, for this relief much thanks,' he said. 'Do you imagine that our friend, the Bard of Avon, ever foresaw the use to which some of his immortal lines would be put, or should I say adapted?'

'I'm afraid I've no idea.'

It did not seem possible that this would continue for a plane journey of one hour and twenty minutes. On the other hand there did not seem to be anything that could prevent it.

Hilda Manningham was seated against the window of the

lounge, her costume and appearance making the other travellers look like a group of refugees nearing the end of their long journey.

'My dear, poor you!' she said. 'Can't we get you away from this beastly little man?'

'I don't think so.'

'I thought the Irish were supposed to be such *wonderful* talkers.'

'It's a gift which can work either way.'

'Pardon me, ladies and gentlemen and *mes enfants,*' said Mr Neelan returning, 'but I feel constrained to absent me from the felicity of your company for some moments, owing to running almost literally at the portals of the ahh . . . well, far be it from me in the presence of a lady . . . as you were! Where was I?'

'You ran into someone,' said Patrick.

'Oh yes. James Lynch, by name, more popularly known as Jim. Used to be with me in that little project extracting the water from turf, until I decided it was rather like Moses and the rock and took to curtains. Ahh, there he is.'

Mr Lynch came out of the Gentlemen's, kept his eyes averted, and chose a seat at the other side of the room.

'Curtains?' said Patrick.

'Yes, you know, for the English romantics. I speak not of that literary movement in which you and I are well grounded, but hints of the gorse in the Wicklow hills, mingling with a faintly pink suggestion of the fucshia of West Kerry, joined with the brown of the Mayo bogs and the purple of a Donegal twilight. Good colours all the same. They sold well, until I decided to switch to cement. Never leave it too late. Am I right?'

'I'm sure you are,' said Patrick.

'Ahh.'

The call had come. They moved out. Now it was beginning. Displaced persons moving with happy expectation into the green plane, welcomed by the pretty smiling hostesses in green; partly across the water in that sane and only place, home, already.

'You stay by me, Patrick. Get in there by the window. I don't care to look out. I value my skin too dearly.'

Hilda sat across the way and was soon separated from them by a priest.

Mr Neelan entangled the safety-belts, exclaiming and sweating and growing alarmed. The plane was filled with sunshine, and his face had turned red. But he still wore his coat and hat.

'Say a prayer for us,' he whispered confidently to the priest who looked surprised.

'God be with us, are we off?'

'Yes. She told us not to smoke.'

'Good Lord,' said Mr Neelan, pulling the wet butt out of his mouth and driving it into the ash-tray which Patrick found for him.

The plane warmed up and slowly started off. Rapidly it gathered momentum. The pincers descended on Patrick's elbow and gradually closed tighter and tighter until he thought that he must surely scream. Then they were in the air, and they relaxed, leaving his arm and hand without the power of movement.

Mr Neelan drew out a handkerchief and wiped his dripping face.

'Praise be to God, are we up?'

'Yes.'

There was an announcement about smoking and refreshments to which Mr Neelan listened with his mouth open and an expression of rapt attention as if anything said under these conditions must be of profound importance. Then he took off his hat, laid it on his lap, and wiped his balding head.

A moment later he had halted the air hostess, who was walking quickly down the aisle, by catching hold of the tail of her short green coat.

'Now, then,' he said, 'let us take stock. Well, well, we're in luck. Where, as the song used to say, before your time, my dear, and our friend's here too, did you get those lovely eyes?'

'I'll attend to you in a m . . .'

'I'll take a large glass of the elixir. Irish and proud of it. And this lady?' he said, calling out to Hilda, past the priest.

'I'll have a brandy.'

'Ah, *le cognac.*'

'We've only Hennessey,' said the hostess, rather curtly.

Hilda nodded.

'*C'est la même chose,*' said Mr Neelan, seeming to hesitate about the priest, and then decide against it. 'And my friend here . . . ?'

Patrick ordered a whisky too. It seemed the only hope.

They were away above the clouds.

'I told them some good stories. D'you know the one about Jimmy Dunne, the Mad Archer?'

'No.'

'Well, I told them that for a start.'

Thousands of feet aloft in the sky. Sealed in a small cylinder, spancelled together.

'They don't have much humour of their own, you know. I don't know where he dragged Falstaff from. Probably an Irishman, or was he Welsh? No, no, that was . . . Anyhow, I play up a little, between you and me, strictly between *entre nous* you understand? Though mind you there's no one I detest more than the Irish boyo putting it on in England. I can't stand all that drinking, and dirt, like yourself no doubt. I'm a stickler for morality and I'm not going to be so damned mealy-mouthed as not to admit it. That Sleator, the painter so-called, who was in all their papers a few months back, for reasons I prefer not to name in your presence—most embarrassing for me when I arrive, bad for business altogether, bad for the country.' Mr Neelan, who was already red, was turning scarlet. 'Disgusting, foul, verminous, obscene—and an insult to the Church. Of course all that goes down very well across the water. They fall for it every time. Your mother knows him, I believe. Well, she must be a very broad-minded woman. But let not you and I be contentious. They took me over one of these New Towns. They've some ideas, but they lack the golden virtue, imagination. Give me the man that has imagination and I will wear him on my heart. . . . This is a large one. They're treating us well, are they not?'

'Yes, they are.'

The seats were closer together than in the bus. The elbow grip was almost embarrassingly intimate and the dropping ash more alarming.

'But it's good for me, you know, keeps me up to the mark. These chaps are in the swim. There's a grave temptation to, as it were, subside among us. A fault of which I am less guilty than most, I may say, in all humility. I wouldn't lay it at your feet either?'

Mr Neelan suddenly drew his head away, to focus on Patrick from a better distance.

'Well, I don't know. I'm afraid . . .'

'Of course between the *via media* and the ultimate there are many . . . ahh . . . come on, come on . . . find it for me . . .'

'Gradations?'

Again he moved away and looked back, but with an expression of elaborate surprise this time, followed by a nodding of the head to show admiration and approval.

'Aha. As I thought. A man of learning. A communal spirit. Tell me, ahh, Patrick . . .'

Mr Neelan brought his head right down low, showing its bald top, and massaged Patrick's arm.

'Do you hope to continue your estate. I mean, of course, after a sad event, ah, far off, I hope and trust, but, it will come when it will come and so forth. Do you feel for the land?'

'Well, I don't quite know . . .'

'Does your mother?'

'I shouldn't think it's likely. But I hadn't really thought . . .'

'Quite, quite. Too soon, too soon. *Festina lente.* I go beyond my brief. Fathers, unfortunately, must act upon the future, and you've got sixty acres there.'

Mr Neelan, what are you talking about?'

'Aha, I show thee a mystery, eh? Drink up. I myself I may say, have come to believe profoundly in the land, but cities are cities, and they must grow. Apart from that—and only apart from that —our dear country is agricultural or it's nothing. That is what I propose to tell them. Indeed I have done so already.'

'I see.'

'Of course, women are a strange breed, of infinite variety doubtless, but fickle . . . *cherchez la femme*. They move badly.'

'Not all of them surely?'

'Yes, all. They grow accustomed to one place.'

'I don't honestly follow you, Mr Neelan. Do you mean that none of them can walk properly?'

'*Move,* my dear fellow. My dear wife wouldn't walk a step and her driving, I may say, alarms me.'

'Oh.'

'They also have short sight.'

'All of them?'

'All of them.'

'I must say it never occurred to me before.'

'You are young. They cannot see ahead. The land will be kind to me, I'll tell you that.'

Occasional sense had turned to madness. The voice went on, and on, and on, until the plane began to lose height. The clouds were thick, like fog, and then, all at once, there was Howth, bright in the sunshine, and through the far windows the evocative, nostalgic, ever-marvellous line of the Dublin mountains. Their two homes were there. Everything seemed to bind them. They had consumed more whisky and this bound them too.

'It's an enterprise I see in my dreams, and something compels me to mention it to you, the first living soul,' said Mr Neelan. 'It springs not basically from sentiment, you'll understand. It's time we put all that aside, God knows—and I'm not forgetting that my own father lost an entire plate-glass window in his O'Connell Street shop in 1916. I used to travel for him later on, you know— typewriters—but I sold the business when he died. Not profitable.

Between you and me, and let it go no further, it would have been better for me if he'd lost more than a window. Another gentleman in the building trade that I could name, one Charlie Gerraty, whose father was the famous Seamus, has profited by it. But I bear no grudge against the old boy. I can say that in all honesty. Though perhaps . . .' Mr Neelan drove his elbow into Patrick's chest. . . . 'it gives me all the more reason to forget the past. No, no, my enterprise would be intended as a final testament to those times, and one by which incidentally I should hope to leave my mark upon the capital—and after that, let us get *on,* get moving, as some of us are, thank God. Where was I?'

'Your enterprise.'

'Ah, yes. A vast modern building, by Gerraty—who more suitable? I bear envy towards none. The largest in the city. Standing where Parnell Square stands now, dominating the whole of O'Connell Street and all beyond. . . .'

Mr Neelan was fastening his safety-belt without looking. All his alarms appeared to have fled.

'Here will be tabulated and filed, for every Irish Sunday newspaper—as long as the alternative remains censored—for every British and American film company, every Fleet Street man who wants to write a book about it, and every living Irish playwright, the accounts of every single rural ambush and street foray that ever honoured our famous battle. And on another floor, pictures of all kinds, stills and reels, and tape-recorded interviews with surviving veterans. And on, say, the tenth floor, a complete library of all memoirs, plays and 1916 to 21 novels. And in the hallway, busts of the heroes.'

The plane landed, with a bump, amidst the sunlight and the green. Mr Neelan did not notice.

'And over the main doorway, inscribed in gold, on concrete, will be written the words—"Memory House". D'you see?'

The Major bent over, inserted the two-pronged fork, eased out of the world a cluster of green leaves the size of a florin, and picking this blight off the fork placed it in a wicker basket on top of its obnoxious relatives. He vaguely felt the action to be creative, like plucking a word from a sentence. With the spoon-shaped under-side of his tool he patted down a tiny circle of mud, and suffered another onset of blackness so that he straightened up to let it pass, giving his head a couple of shakes with his eyes closed.

They opened, no longer blind, on the house, benevolently watching over him in the gentle light of the declining sun. It was a perfect Palladian miniature. Its pillars at either side of the hall-door, and the triangles supported above, were elegant rather than imposing. Seven windows of lovely proportions ran along the first and second floors under the tall roof, and there were three, larger by exactly the right degree, at either side of the entrance and its flight of stone steps. The tops of the squat basement win-dows, behind bars, were just visible above the grass bank. It was grey but not gloomy. The window-frames had recently been painted white, which had cost him a shattering sum, and virginia creeper spread haphazardly about and was now turning red.

To surrender it to Neelan would be the same as handing his own child over, at a price, to the vivisectionist.

He saw another dandelion, hitched the stool towards it with his left hand and speared it with his right. They were habitual move-ments and they occupied his mind no more than lighting a pipe. His own child was home, and almost a stranger. The only appar-ent proof that she was Grania, who had shown a talent for draw-ing and was outstanding at lacrosse at Alexandra College, was that she reminded him of her mother, and yet this was presumably quite possible for a stranger. Also he did not want to be reminded of her mother. There had been too much pain.

Women who were neither brainless nor silent made life a crucifixion.

Mary Cullen had cooked one of her roasts, but it was pork, and she had followed it with apple pie. At his solitary lunch Finola Doyle had served him with these two dishes which Mary at least should know were poison to his peculiar system. He had never liked to offend the servants, who were in a position that no human being should hold towards another, and one which in addition they might quit at the fall of an incautious word. So now he suffered yet another spasm of dizziness, and straightened his already military back and waited.

He did not look in the least enfeebled. He was a small, wiry man with close-cropped gingery grey hair and moustache, and a little nose broken in a fall at the stone wall at Amsterdam in 1926. Major Murrough-Bryant was still a name known all over the equestrian world, though the representatives of that world only saw him once a year, at the Dublin Horse Show. He was frequently available at race-meetings, which was of course not quite the same thing. His fellow countrymen would scarcely have considered him available at all at the Horse Show. The approaches were made by foreigners. Once the adornment of the Royal Dublin Society, he had gradually broken with it. Nor, indeed, did he hold any official position in racing. He had maintained a couple of horses for a time, but they too had been abandoned. The neighbouring countryside, which had already been severely restricted, was still further reduced by the encroachments of Mr Neelan and the like, and the invincible objection to hunting was the nature of the people with whom one was compelled to hunt. This latter objection covered the whole of his retreat. There was little temptation to serve among the administrators of equestrianism when one was a fervent admirer of the works of Keats. Finally, as regards the missing horses, there was economy; and there was also, perhaps, a little indulgence in self-denial.

If Grania, his neglectful daughter who was as good on a horse as she was at lacrosse, had shown persistence, it might have been different. But to her Horse Show Week now meant something in which horses played virtually no part whatsoever. As for Patrick, he had never mounted one, despite repeated invitations to do so.

How was his grandson to be addressed and advised, the Major wondered, rising from the stool because it would be embarrassing to be found dead on the lawn. When he stood up the old coat and trousers hung about him, and the trousers nearly fell off. In the past he had been immaculate in tweed-coat and riding-breeches, but even now, when going to work, he was dapper.

Advising anyone was presumptuous and almost certainly futile, particularly in the case of Patrick. He had been permitted to see very little of the young man and did not know whether he was a genuine traveller in this world or an ass. Yet some form of address would be necessary, because the time had come to inquire whether or not he wished this place, his ultimate inheritance, to go to the knackers.

He also hated asking questions, and had not asked one for fifty-two years. (Fanny had said: 'Yes, acushla.')

Trench had come up from the drive from his gate-lodge, bearing two pink pots, and was evidently on the way to his garden and greenhouse at the rear. He would have to be taken to whatever small suburban villa by the sea was selected, perched in the back of the Vauxhall with his hat on his knees, and he alone would be stricken in a manner comparable to the Major.

'Afternoon, Major,' he said, pausing and looking through the wire netting in an appreciative manner at the lawn. For years it had been his employer's pitiful folly—to Trench a criminal retreat for the greatest horseman of his day—but slowly he had learned respect, and it was now the best lawn west of Dublin.

This view was more like him. He was plump, with two waist-coats, and a good trustworthy red-veined face. He had been gardener at Edenmore for almost thirty years, following his father in that position. He represented the old values so much that it was only from time to time, with a shock, that the Major became aware that the waistcoats were ragged and awful, and above them was a filthy shirt, with no collar, revealing the buttoned top of a woollen undervest grey with dirt.

'Afternoon, Trench,' he said, coming out on to the drive.

'She's looking well.'

'Ah, I'm afraid there's not much point in it.'

An expression of profound melancholy came over the Major's sensitive face. He placed his hands on his hips and looked as if he was preventing his week-end clothes from dropping off him.

'It's just an amusement, you know.'

Trench gave him a quick glance, and was almost laughing.

'You always take the gloomy view, Major.'

'Ah, well . . . you know how it is. What keeps *you* so happy, Trench?'

'I couldn't really say, Major. I never believed in worrying. I suppose Herself did enough for the two of us.'

Trench looked a little sad.

His adored wife had astonishingly passed a long life with a disease that meant her bones were like matchwood. A year ago she had fallen on the step outside the gate-lodge and died almost at once. Mention of her recalled another fact about Trench of which the Major was only conscious at rare moments. She had been a hopelessly enslaved Catholic, almost living in the village church, and Trench, if not exactly enslaved, was one too. It was almost impossible to remember, except at those equally rare moments when one noted the condition of his underclothes.

'You should be thinking of finding yourself some nice young girl in the village, Trench. It must be hard for you to manage.'

Trench's face was all happiness again.

'I'd never find one like her, Major. But it had crossed my mind.

Not for me. But to teach that boy of mine some sense. Mick needs a mother's hand. He was really too much for Herself.'

Mick, who even in appearance was an inexplicable offshoot of these two good people, had joined the Irish Army where, in his father's mind, he was ultimately to become a Major; which of course was nothing like being a Major in the British Army, but it was good enough. There had been trouble, and he had left quickly. Then there had been the hope of his at least following his father in loyal service at Edenmore, but he had found work in the garden 'a bloody bore'. Finally, the Major had placed him behind one of the counters in his shop in town, and had already received one complaint which he had kept from Trench.

'The latest is he wants to go over the other side. Tells me they're modern over there, and so on. He's gone mad on all this jazz music business.'

'Well, I should let him go, Trench. The world is only across the water, and the infection travels. Some catch it and some don't. It's a true division, unlike the one our politicians make so much play with, and it has rather profound implications. Once caught, it can only be cured by going to meet it, and even then I'm not so sure. Shaw pointed out how few of them return, in spite of their songs of home. Being immune, I've always viewed it with detachment and, I think, clarity. Living on the edge of the times can be very interesting, you know, no matter how hateful they appear. But the existence of my grandson has quite suddenly given the subject a more urgent and confusing importance.'

'Yes,' said Trench. He liked the way the Major sometimes talked slowly, in sentences, even though they were unintelligible.

'What's Master Patrick going to do?' he asked.

'I don't know, Trench. That's really the point.'

'Well, I've never been infected, as you call it, Major, thank God. Mick's off tonight with that Finola, to some ballroom or other.'

'Really? Perhaps she'll be better than a mother.'

'What! That one? Ha, ha, ha. No, no. I don't think so, Major.'

They talked a little more, about the garden, the races at Baldoyle that afternoon, and the prospects for the Irish Rugby fifteen. Nature alone was all right, and sport was the only activity safe from the relentless cackle of the opinionated. Then they separated, and the Major went up and into the dark hall where his father's deer stood out from the oak panels, high up, and a suit of armour stood guard beside the huge fireplace. He did not care for deer or armour, but cared deeply for preserving the past, which was so much more preferable than the present and future —though that was discussable.

Finola had just appeared in the doorway that led to the kitchen basement, looking fat and pretty in her cap and apron and watching him with a curiously puzzled expression. For some reason he said: 'I'm going to lie down for a while, Finola,' before he mounted the wide stairs.

It would be foolish to confuse dyspepsia with old age, he thought, with some difficulty making the first landing where the missing picture by A. E. had left a rectangle slightly lighter than the rest of the panelling. He had extremely little apprehension about dying. Yet while one lived, and even more so with time running out, there was the need of communication. But with whom, in this community of shackled minds?

In the top-floor corridor he felt odd, and paused at a window. Grania's room, which used to be her mother's when privacy became imperative to her, was at the end, and the only bedroom that looked out on this side. Beyond the tennis-court the lovely landscape immediately called upon the imagination, the only human quality of any importance whatever. The London plane was droning away somewhere up in the blue, but otherwise present and past slept together in the stillness of the autumn afternoon. For him, at least, the past was there too, for he had lived here a very long time. Everything on this western side was part of him. Whichever fields he had not ridden, because of cunningly fortified hedgerows and threats of prosecution and death, he had walked. And he had looked on it over and over again, at all hours and seasons. It was simple and gave a kind of comfort, especially in the evenings: merely fields which gradually became totally devoid of trees, rising to a curving skyline across which the clouds drifted incessantly. Over the other side, through the Pine Forest, one came on the open plains from which the backward view was spread much wider, with the Hell-Fire Club as a centre-piece on the highest hill. This was more modest. He preferred it. After his numerous riding commitments abroad had ended, he had only left it twice. The real odyssey was internal, and these few miles were ample. At times he picked up books in the library with surprise, and then disinterest: people found it necessary to investigate North Africa, and do six months in a Greek monastery, and undergo a perpetual repetition of suffering in squalid cities. In Paris his appearance in the ring had always been in the balance owing to the near-certainty of food-poisoning. His two departures since had been to London, on enforced business trips, where to avoid the surrounding stink of human corruption he had passed all the spare hours between trains seated in the lounge of the Euston Hotel, reading Montaigne.

But the view had one feature which had formerly struck no discord, because it was attractive, but was now turned to a permanent challenge. It was the Neelans' pink residence sitting on top of the nearest eminence; and seeing it he felt a little sick.

His handsome, bearded father, and his mother, looking subdued and humble, which was deceptive, were on the wall behind him. His father had been an eminent Dublin surgeon, formerly of the Royal Army Medical Corps, who believed that both sons should go nowhere else but Sandhurst. Considering the ultimate careers of himself and his dubious brother Harry in Kenya, it had perhaps been pointless. But it had equipped him for very early distinction, through hell, in the fields of France.

The wall above them was showing damp and mildew where it met the ceiling—but who was going to pay for that? When he entered his bedroom the floor, under the worn carpet, groaned and creaked, and some day it would go through to his study below. It was cold, but he seldom felt the cold and never admitted it. The windows overlooked the long concrete yard with its cowsheds, empty stables, and garages for his Vauxhall and his daughter's Bentley, when it was home. Above the garages were rooms occupied, when *he* was 'home,' by Grania's sycophantic panderous pimp, Flanagan. Beyond were the long herbaceous borders, and a doorway through into the large vegetable garden— all of it surrounded by a red-brick wall in urgent need of restoration. Then there was the parkland, with huge trees and cattle beneath them. The farming and the cowsheds were given to a man named Duffy in the village, for an absurdly small annual payment. It was hard enough even to keep up the gardens, without running a farm, and the Neelans' farm-boy, Paddy, now looked in to help Trench on two afternoons a week, since Mick had decided that it was dull.

Beyond was the sea. It was not so sweepingly presented as in the vista of which Mrs Neelan had grown weary. It was a thin line of blue, partly backed by Howth, seen above low hills and here and there clusters of new red houses. The nearest cluster, for which Mr Neelan was responsible, was mercifully hidden by trees.

The Major sat on his bed, removed his gumboots, which had barely been touching the floor because he was so small, and lay down. His wardrobe door was open, showing, glued to the inside, photographs of two Parisian actresses, one of them in her negligée, equipped with a long cigarette-holder. These were souvenirs of a visit to the French capital in 1923, when in spite of continually threatened food-poisoning and his riding commitments, he had read to both of them, to their surprise and delight, from the works of Yeats. He was not an ordinary equestrian, even then, and was, moreover, very elegant, handsome and witty. At home Fanny had already begun her appalling decline.

Ireland had re-embraced him for the first time in London, on leave during the British war, in the person of his future wife, which was not so strange. She was lovely, and it was then *she* who did the reading, in a room in Bloomsbury. She read him Yeats and Synge and Shaw, and an infinity of Irish legends. She persuaded him, a young major back from the nightmare of France, to believe in fairies. Ireland was their country; it was, she added for his sake, the country of the horse; and it was magical. It was also, to her mind, under the yoke, but she did not say that then. The magic was not false, even now, any more than Yeats and Synge. Much of it was there still, in spite of the decay.

The decay had started, for him personally, with a raging fire in the basement. That was after they had settled in Edenmore as man and wife, and after the yoke had been lifted, only to result in civil war. Some assumption that a man with a title gained in the former enemy's forces must be allied with the new Free State had called forth a visit by masked emissaries of the opposition. Local youths who were immediately identifiable appeared one windy night, and with many stuttering apologies—'Ordhers is ordhers, Major'—set fire to paraffin rags in the maids' bedrooms. He had tried to calm his two daughters, meanwhile carrying out as many valuables as possible, while Fanny stood with them on the lawn in her nightdress, in a daze, with three first editions under her arm.

Since he had been permitted, even encouraged, to call the fire brigade, it was soon extinguished, but so was the terrible beauty, and Fanny was never the same. Patriotism had displaced every other resort; and perhaps he had not needed her sufficiently. Soon their two daughters had walked away, with ease and confidence, into an astonishingly different modern world.

He himself had opened a shop that sold riding equipment, fishing-rods and guns. With his name and his business sense—yet another of his abilities—it had flourished and given birth to a smaller branch in Galway. It was in Dublin's West End, but to his way of thinking it only just survived the Protestant stigma and was a poor match for the income tax commissioners.

But there were things to be said about the present, and he was now writing them, though limited as always by his commission, to the state of the island in which he lived. They lay on the table beside him. It was the fifth draft of an article he was composing at the surprising, and flattering—for there was still virtue in the West—behest of the *Ballynoggin Star*. The given subject was 'Factories or Farms?' His second page lay uppermost and he began to read it:

'And although one is reluctant to accept as inevitably axiomatic that the vulgarity of a civilisation's outward show is correlative to the degree to which the qualitative values are inherent in the community, one is nevertheless forced to conclude, if the foregoing evidence is considered valid, that in this country at the present time there is an undeniable consanguinity between spiritual decay and approaching economic ruin, individual pusillanimity being the common relative and the Church its doting parent.'

He picked up a pencil from the table, and, with a sense of satisfaction, took out the word 'inevitably'. The last six words were a temporary indulgence. They were satisfying now, but they would have to come out in the end, for the sake of survival.

After this he felt odd again, and could do no more. He lay back on the pillow. He was going to be in a very bad mood when they arrived.

chapter six

Norah Gerraty lay on the scarlet, nylon-covered couch and looked past a copy of *Vogue* through Jolainin's speciality, an entire wall of glass, at her husband crossing the hill on a hired horse. The sun was going down, and the prospect made her shiver, although the hidden heating made the room extremely hot. It was a foolish reaction, she realised, since riding must obviously be a warm occupation, even though she had never seen him spur the horse beyond a walk.

She felt sleepy and filled with vague thoughts and apprehensions; which was assisted by the Stanley Black orchestra, playing softly through the hidden amplifiers. The lunch party had been rather mysterious, although there was an explanation for it which presumably applied once more. Moira Neelan's rôle had at least been clear. She had seen the symptoms often enough, and in Moira's case they were blatant. But Charlie had not been particularly attentive.

This might have been put down to the presence of his wife, except that it had never proved an obstacle to him in the past. On the other hand it might mean that he felt himself to be genuinely involved this time, which would be still more unusual. Women appeared to be roughly the same in other countries, but Irish men were unique. At Cannes he had indeed become casino-mad, but only after arousing the affections of someone called Yvonne, who had declared her despair to Norah. That, too, was a familiar experience.

She had a double vision in which the horse and rider were impressive, moving across the spectacular Wicklow landscape, and yet the rider was Charlie, and she wondered what, if anything, was passing through his mind. One could comprehend everything else: fields and hedges, a few feeble copies of their own house, Sugarloaf mountains, and away to the left the hump back of Bray Head with a misty intimation of the sea beside it. On both the setting and the house, which Charlie had generously named Finlandia, they had come together again in a surprising and exciting way. The exterior was his, the interior hers. They were now apart at the usual distance; the house was complete; and essentially the only joy that remained was the surprise on the faces of the people who came to see it.

It was different when Andrew and Vernon were at home, particularly Vernon, who shared her taste for furnishings and was sensitive. The older boy was like his father. Only two weeks previously they had sent Vernon off for the first time to Downside and it had affected her deeply, left the place empty, and left her with the sensation that she must start to live some life of her own again.

Andrew would return and work in Dublin, probably at architecture. That was all right. But for Vernon she wanted something better. After Downside he must go to France. There she dreamed of him marrying a French girl of an aristocratic family, with a château, which she would visit; moving to Paris, meeting a count or two, mixing in Catholic circles of quality. They had friends at home, and she liked some of them. She had cultivated the few people of taste: Terence Keogh, the Royal Hibernian Academician who had painted both her and Moira Neelan; Dan Lavelle, Ireland's first male couturier 'Teeth' Murphy, the dentist on the Arts Council. But attending Mass at Cannes had opened her eyes to very different possibilities, with Compte Philippe de Malmoison and his admittedly young and beautiful wife seated in the pew ahead. It had only been emphasised by the curious Protestant contrast in the hotel, of Mrs Agerton-Willy, who was not young, and her count, who was not French, not young either, and not married to her.

Charlie was mounting the hill now, to the house of the farmer who owned the animal. He was preparing to make a first appearance with the Bray Harriers, and she felt that he should really hurry up and try the first experience of trotting. His coat and breeches were both made in Savile Row. They went with the house, but she still from time to time remembered Paul Casey in ragged jacket and filthy trousers, with straw in his hair and mud in his finger-nails, conducting the harvesting in the summer fields at Blessington. It had been well over a year ago, when Charlie was in America, examining the work of Frank Lloyd Wright. Paul was doing it now as a member of the staff in the agricultural college at Cirencester, and she had not troubled, or perhaps been moved, to interest anyone since.

Now Vernon had gone too.

She really must remember to drop a note to the theatre, to Hugo Lorrimer in advance of his arrival next month; not to mention booking seats. She had been to the first night of several pre- and post-London productions which had made it plain that to give full vent to all one's impulses, vocal and physical, was vitality, and the rest was anæmia, and she had expectations that the lesson would be made still more plain by *The Kiss of Death*.

She was aware of odd yearnings. She was distantly touched, once again, by the womanly feeling that when you have a husband, children and home, the only worthwhile thing to be done is to find some available gentleman and strip him to his socks.

But she decided that it was probably the heating and Stanley Black and examined afresh the attractions of the room, wondering if there was anything that could still be added to it.

The window wall had a rolled bamboo screen at the top, which shot down at the press of a button. It kept the cold out in winter and the sun out in summer. Another button directed the black and primrose curtain across in front of it. At the centre of the shining parquet floor was a marble table, three inches from the ground, in the shape of a 'cello, on which were collected quaint shells from Bray beach and miniature cacti. There was a larger marble table, cleared for tea, representing a double-bass. There were also two yellow chairs like inverted straw hats on black

pins, and one big deep one, in scarlet, with a button for turning
the television on or off attached to one arm. The set stood against
one of the two end walls, with a Mexican voodoo figure, picked
up by Charlie in America, standing on top of it, his arms outstretched. On these two walls, which were papered in primrose
and white Regency stripes, there were still a few empty spaces,
and these were a persistent challenge. At present they exhibited
in a quaint and charming pattern an abundance of shells, a number of ancient pistols and hunting-horns collected on travels
abroad, some colourful examples of Finnish and Aran Island
crochet-work, two brilliant pictures by Dermot Sleator, dripping
with paint—she would not have him in the house, but one could
still recognise genius—and as a centre-piece, by which Charlie
had been genuinely touched, the I.R.A. badge of Seamus Gerraty,
surrounded by a tiny wreath of seagulls' feathers, also collected
by Vernon on Bray beach.

There was room for more shells. It was a delightfully artistic
decoration, of which no one else in Dublin would have been capable in a million years. Behind her, as she lay on the low couch,
which was too short for her long legs, the fourth wall was of
glass, looking into the dining-room. It was charming. The table
and chairs were of curling ironwork, painted white. The table-
top was of heat-proof glass, and the seats of the chairs were done
in crimson plush. Here there was definitely nothing more to be
added.

She felt intensely bored, and rose suddenly and wandered
across the hallway, which was only divided from the sitting-
room by a wall of bamboos and leafy rubber-plants. At the end of
the corridor she could hear Alfredo and Angelina singing softly
in Italian. It was nearly tea-time. She stood at the door of the
bedroom and looked with satisfaction at the bedspread edged
with mink. Above the end hung a crucifixion by a modern Italian
artist, which she had come on with great relief in a shop of advanced taste in Grafton Street, because it was such a change

from the usual native vulgarity. Finally she went into the bathroom next door and washed her hands and face.

It was a cool room, and one suitable to reflection. The walls were papered with enlarged under-water photographs, dark blue in colour, with an octopus groping for the bath taps. It was really the most imaginative idea of all. She was reflecting that the real trouble with her fellow-countrymen was a total incapacity to take on any of the commonly recognised civilised virtues. They had achieved it in this house, but they were alone in their achievement. My God, other people's houses! It would take them another thirty years to abandon their veneered wardrobes and the beige wallpaper with the thin border of flowers. They had only just got round to disposing of the pianola. In his occupation Charlie at least knew all about that, and had suffered from it. And as for the inhabitants, they were still in the dark back room of a rural pub: the women flirtatious, the men thirsty. It lurked there on formal occasions behind the attempt at being like other nationalities. The most recent experience which she had been compelled to undergo, was at the dance of Contemporary Tweed Incorporated. The first few hours of assumed dignity rendered them mute and uneasy in their unspeakable clothes. The men's evening trousers were so wide that they appeared to have no feet. An hour later they were indeed footless; happy at last, the hopeless pretence over. It was one of the still persisting charms of Charlie that he could make and hand some undeserving woman a real martini without pouring it down her bosom. Yet without the example of civilised company, he too degenerated. She had attempted to throw a few little dinner-parties since they came to Finlandia, and Alfredo and Angelina had spent most of the following morning disposing of the broken glass. Oh, for somewhere where people said 'How do you do' occasionally, and 'So nice to see you', and 'Would you care to sit beside——?' and candles were not regarded as a dirty joke.

Having washed her face, she was not too pleased with the length of her nose and the proximity of her eyes, and she at once put on make-up from a cabinet shaped like a dolphin's mouth, and combed her hair. Then she wandered back towards the sitting-room.

The afternoon had been interminable. She should have gone to the Baldoyle races. She had felt a curious reluctance to meet the people she knew would be there, and Charlie was now obsessed with the ambition to control a horse on his own account, because there were two other architects riding with the Bray Harriers.

Tonight they were dining and dancing at the Gresham with the Callinans, and she felt no more enthusiastic about meeting them again. She had seen just enough of the Callinans at Cannes, from which they were the sole available survivors. The Brophys had been fighting with each other there, and she had no reason to assume that Dublin had brought them peace. David Keely, James Larkin and Kevin Barry had all three stayed on in Paris, which was of course a schoolboy joke to them. They could not mention it without metaphorically whistling. They would be quite safe.

She was back on the couch, having derived nothing from her little excursion. This was no country for women. The reason they were repeating an extremely familiar foursome with the Callinans was that there was absolutely nothing else to do in this capital city. It was, in a way, a consolation that the dancing ended on the stroke of midnight, when the whole metropolis promptly blacked out. Charlie was useless with the bare minimum of available artistic people whom she had cultivated, and in any case they were not much given to dressing up and dancing. But she would have them at her house-warming next month.

The recollection of this undertaking at once produced a twinge of alarm. Was there any conceivable hope of staging it as it should be staged, without breakages?

She was about to answer this question in the negative when she saw Charlie, through the bamboo plants, coming in and dropping his yellow gloves on the hall tray—the outspread hands of a mendicant, sculpted by Fergus O'Toole in his Cork studios. Facing him as he entered, on the only solid wall large enough to contain it, was her portrait which Terence Keogh had shown at the last Royal Hibernian Academy exhibition. He did not look at it. She wondered how it struck him when he did look at it. Dublin life presented few temptations to live up to such a moment. Yet she doubted very much if Charlie had the wit to make unflattering comparisons. Terence had captured her wearing an enigmatic smile on her bright lips, in her off-the-shoulder black velvet ball-dress, her elegant hands with long red finger-nails folded on her lap. She had been very happy with it. The picture was essentially her, and if Charlie did have doubts, she could reproduce it with very little trouble.

He joined her in the sitting-room, subsiding with an exhausted noise into one of the inverted hats.

She pretended to read *Vogue.* In fact, it occasionally pained her to look at him at all, and however much he merged with the décor she felt that way now. It was partly explained by his behaviour at lunch.

'Phew!' He made the noise again. The chair threw his long legs upwards, so that when she did steal a glance she found his face almost obscured by his knees in their elegant breeches. It was a lined-by-experience, handsome face which familiarity had shown to be deceptive, with wavy black hair which she had never seen disturbed, even in bed. The fixed parting was usually pink, but Cannes had made it brown.

Why did he never read a book? He only read architectural journals. But when she considered it, she realised that there were only about six books in the house, and all of them belonged to Vernon.

'That was good,' he said. He was looking out at the terrain he had conquered. 'It's a great bloody game, and no mistake.'

At their very first meeting it had surprised her that it was possible to look like Gregory Peck and to speak like a character in one of those dreary slum plays by O'Casey. It had passed almost at once. But now she could recapture it.

'What was the game over lunch?' she asked.

'What?'

It seemed to take five minutes for him to react, look at her, and speak.

'Lunch. What was it all about? I'd just like to know for once. Moira is by the way of being a friend of mine.'

'Moira?'

'That's right. Neelan.'

'Ha, ha, ha!'

He had this sudden, empty, bellowing laugh which was too vulgar for words.

'Oh, Norah, my dear, you're sometimes very wrong.'

'I see.'

'Ha, ha. By God, she talks. Like an old hen. But God help her, she's lively enough. Ah, I suppose she's all right.'

'Good. Why this sudden interest, then, in the Neelans?'

'We-ell, it's a little business matter. It's dear old Tommy who's the subject of interest. All above board, you may be sorry to hear. I'm investigating on behalf of one of our religious orders—admittedly in the hopes of their patronage. They want to know his intentions, without concerning themselves openly in the matter.'

'I can't pretend to understand.'

'Or care?'

'Except that Tom Neelan seems to have become important all of a sudden. He's going up for Senator, it seems.'

'What!'

'So Moira said.'

'Good Christ!' He slapped one of his elegant knees. 'Well, that beats everything. That really beats everything. What else did she say? Your womanly wiles seem to have extracted more than I was able to discover.'

'Something about giving the Murrough-Bryants a shock, but she couldn't say what.'

She had really interested him. He was leaning forward, his boots tucked under the chair.

'Was that all?'

'That was all.'

'I see.'

'I'm glad.'

'Well, well. So we *are* in competition.'

He subsided again, looking more blankly at the view, his hands locked across his chest.

She stifled her interest, which was not difficult, and went on reading an article about Balmain. But after a few moments she was reminding herself again that she must drop a line to the theatre, to Hugo Lorrimer.

chapter seven

Patrick came out of his room and paused in the corridor, held by the sudden startling spectacle of a full moon rising in the night sky. All else was blackness, except for tiny spots of light in two of the windows of the Neelans' house away in the dark, a small human refuge in a natural vastness that one tended to forget in London.

He paused again on the first-floor landing because his mother was standing in the small sitting-room ahead of him. She had changed into a black shirt and tight red trousers. The shirt matched her silky black hair. She looked extraordinarily young, and was smoking a cigarette in a long black holder.

'Hallo, darling,' she said. 'I was wondering if I should do anything about this room.'

'An odd idea after all these years.'

'But not too late, I trust. I've decided I'm going to stay till Christmas at least, and I intend to leave my mark this time.'

'You interest me.'

They looked at the room. It was barely furnished, having a settee with a faded cover in petit-point, a Sheraton writing-desk and chair and a high-backed arm-chair by a white fluffy hearth-rug. Above the desk were shelves displaying a silver shield, silver cups of many sizes, and all the trophies won by the Major on horseback. But the dominant feature was Grania's mother, above the white Adam mantelpiece, painted by Sir John Lavery. She lay on a couch looking wan and beautiful, with books by her side. The Major used this room when he was alone; which was most of the time. Tonight the fireplace was empty because the fire in the large sitting-room below was lit instead. To light both would, in the Major's view, be criminal folly. So the room was cold.

'It's a little severe, don't you think?' said Grania.

'Perhaps he likes it that way.'

'Don't put me off. I hope he's all right, poor dear.'

'Oh, I think so. He's still in his room, but he said he'd be down for dinner.'

'Did he mention your future?'

'No. Not a word. He talked about the garden and so on, and I went out to have a look. It's really a marvellous place.'

'Yes, I think so,' said Grania.

'Unfortunately Hilda came too, and she was wearing the wrong shoes or something.'

'I do hope she'll take off those diamond ear-rings. They're bound to get lost in some field or other. But we mustn't be too hard. She's been through pretty average hell.'

Patrick knew all about her own troubles with Count André, though she had said nothing and he had never met him.

'Where is she?' asked Grania vaguely.

'I think she's downstairs.'

'Oh, there you are, ma'am.'

Finola Doyle, plump and pretty, had suddenly appeared in the doorway, brightly painted for her evening off.

'Yes, Finola?'

Finola did not reply for a moment, as she was examining the red trousers with astonishment.

'I did indeed!' she said, recovering. 'The thing is I just can't get out of Mr Flanagan who's supposed to do what. I don't care for his manner, to be quite frank. In fact, to tell you the truth, I don't really think I can stay.'

'Oh, my God. It was all explained to you, child, the last time we came over. You managed then.'

'That was only for the Horse Show, and it was ages ago, and I can't remember.'

'He serves the meat. You serve the vegetables. He serves the wine. You help each other to clear it away. You bring in the pudding, and he serves it.'

'That's really much too difficult, to be quite frank. I manage perfectly well with the Major. I don't see why it needs a crowd.'

'Because now there is a crowd, as you term it, for dinner, which we are eating early to oblige you. I think in return you might make a slight effort.'

'Effort, is it! Oh well, all right. This once.'

'Tell me, Finola, before you go. I see you've drawn the curtains here. Have you drawn them down in the sitting-room?'

'You might well ask, ma'am! There's *another* thing. I have. But I was in two minds, and the Major'll probably have a fit. He never has them drawn. He likes the night lookin' in. He says it's artificial—or something—to cut it out.'

'I know, I know. Thank you, Finola.'

'Oh, you're welcome.'

She had gone. They could hear her thundering down the stairs.

A moment afterwards they followed. The house was cold. In the hall the oak panelling, deers' heads and suit of armour were gloomy, and no fire was permitted in the huge fireplace. But off the hall was the sitting-room, and it was cheerful, with coal blazing in the grate. It was a large room, with deep armchairs and sofas in faded chintz. Hilda Manningham, dressed as before, was examining the contents of one of the old glass-fronted bookcases. These held a comprehensive library of Irish writing of the past, and there were other reminders of the Renaissance on the pale green walls: prints of drawings of both Yeats and Joyce by Augustus John, and early representations of Men of the West, in pen and wash, by Jack Yeats. Over the mantelpiece was a large, late, vivid Jack Yeats. This was an addition made by Grania, and the only one permitted by her father out of the many contemporary works that she would have purchased if given her way, notably those of Dermot Sleator.

'This is *such* a dear old room,' said Hilda. 'I've quite fallen in love with the place already.'

'I'm delighted to hear it, darling,' said Grania. 'I think we could do with some strong drinks, Patrick.'

'And Patrick took me for such a heavenly walk. It really is green, like they say, and strange somehow. I half expected a dear little leprechaun to pop up out of the grass at any moment.'

'I'm afraid Father has driven them all away.'

'I *am* looking forward to meeting him. I'm told he's sweet.'

'Sometimes.'

Patrick poured them drinks from the bottles which Finola had assembled on the old desk in the corner, and they sat before the fire.

'I'm afraid it's going to be very dull for you both,' said Grania. 'I don't seem to know anyone in Dublin any more, except when they're over for the Horse Show. I had invitations from Lavinia Westmacott and Antoinette Haslipp this morning, but they're a long way off, and I haven't really come over to meet them.'

'Nor have I,' said Patrick. 'I don't want to meet anyone.'

'But still I really must get in touch with Dermott.'

'I don't quite see the necessity,' said Patrick.

'Oh, that's the fabulous, wild Irish painter who's had such a success in London. It would be absolutely fascinating to meet him,' said Hilda.

'Mr Neelan gravely disapproves of him,' Patrick remarked.

'My God, those Neelans are common,' said his mother.

'That frightful little man on the plane,' Hilda agreed.

'Oh, I don't know . . . I thought you overdid it rather at the airport, Mother. He introduced you to his wife and you spoke to her as if she was the cat's dinner.'

'It seemed to me mutual. I suppose she is still suffering from the fact that I freed Finola from their captivity. Not that it was a great gain. Aren't you too hot in your fur, dear?'

'Well, I was a wee bit chilly upstairs. I'll warm up in a minute. I do love your slacks. They're most becoming and frightfully daring.'

'I must say Dublin is marvellous, though,' said Patrick.

'Heaven,' said Hilda.

'It's so friendly and homely after London. I like the thought of being able to find whoever one wants, seated in the same bar, on the same stool, as when one was here before. It's sane and consistent. Like this house.'

'I can't wait to see it all,' said Hilda.

The Major quietly entered the room. He had put on old bedroom slippers and carried two books under one arm. His face wore an expression of apprehension. Patrick rose and pointed out the cause of it, saying:

'Grandfather, this is Hilda Manningham.'

'Well,' he said, bowing and putting on a smile, 'had I known that our guest looked like this, I would have taken greater pains with my costume.'

'Oh, how sweet! But I like it,' said Hilda, examining the dilapidated coat and trousers.

'I expected one of my daughter's more Bohemian friends. No one told me there was going to be anyone like this in the house.'

'Well, I must say,' said Hilda, 'I've never had such a charming reception.'

The Major turned his back to them and began cleaning his pipe on top of the chest-of-drawers near the door. Hilda glanced at Grania and Patrick in slight surprise, evidently seeking an explanation.

'Are you feeling better, Father?' asked Grania.

'I'll live,' he said, in a different voice. 'For a while.'

He turned round, slowly crossed over, poured himself a large whisky, and said:

'This room is like a blast furnace.'

'It's heavenly,' said Hilda.

'It's consuming about six months' supply of fuel, that's the only trouble.'

'Oh, I'm sure you wouldn't grudge it to us,' said Hilda, smiling.

The Major did not reply.

He went and sat on the sofa farthest from the fire, placed his drink and a work by Berdyaev on the table beside him and began reading *The Lovely Corpse*.

'It's my fault,' said Grania. 'I told Finola to build it up. She's already threatened to leave, by the way,' she added to her father, who did not raise his eyes from his book.

'Oh dear, no!' exclaimed Hilda. 'I hope *I'm* not to blame. She seems such a sweet, pretty little thing. A real colleen.'

'She's quite pretty. But they're all impossible. You have to plead with them to do every damn thing, and then they do it wrong.'

'But, my dear, it's the same everywhere.'

'It's a lot worse here. I went and spoke to Mary Cullen in the kitchen this morning, and I had scarcely opened my mouth . . .'

'It's always astonished me,' said the Major, still apparently reading his book, 'that people regard discussion of the servants as a genuinely worthwhile occupation.'

'It's a subject that concerns us, I would have thought,' said Grania, shaking her hair back and looking across the room at him.

'It's more like wallowing in manure.'

There was a pause. Hilda was showing alarm.

'They're human beings,' said Grania.

'So?'

He lifted his pipe from the table and, still reading his book, lit it. Patrick noticed that his hand holding the match was trembling slightly.

'All human beings are of interest, surely?' added Grania.

'That's the current theory. It's natural that when a civilisation is in decay it should assign individual virtues to every speck of rubbish in sight. Ninety-nine per cent of human beings merely exist, that's all. Like Duffy's animals out in the farmyard.'

'Oh, really, Father!'

'What a fantastic idea,' said Hilda.

'And in any case,' said the Major, turning a page of *The Lovely Corpse,* 'the servants merely interest you in so far as they do, or do not, pander correctly to your desires. Like that fawning creature you bring around with you. Still, if you were able to present them with imagination, and with some intimation that you have the faintest notion of what is proceeding inside them, it might be of interest to us. As it is, it's merely female cackle of a superficiality beyond description.'

His face had become a little flushed. He was regularly stroking his moustache with the end of his pipe. With his other hand he turned over a page of his book.

'I think,' said Patrick, 'that Mother meant that everyone has *some* quality. . . .'

'Quality, unfortunately, is what they totally lack. And I'm afraid at my age I no longer have time for anything else.'

'Get us another drink, darling,' said Grania. 'You're simply not interested in people,' she added, as Patrick went to do so. 'I am. In all sorts . . .'

'In so far as they flatter you. But you haven't the faintest inkling of what proceeds inside them.'

'Oh, what nonsense.'

'No, no. You haven't. I mean, I'm sorry, but it's a fact.'

The Major laughed, rather unhappily, and looked at Patrick for agreement.

'But I thought you said that most of them were of no interest, anyhow?' asked Patrick.

'To me, no. But one should have a little humility to recognise that they do have some form of existence, if merely out of what used to be called politeness. That they are simply delinquent slaves is characteristic of female egoism.'

'Why are you especially against women?' said Patrick.

'One advantage of solitude,' said the Major, taking a drink and giving his book a little less attention, 'and having one foot in the grave, is that it presents the opportunity for thought, and the subject of paramount importance and interest is what path mankind is taking. At the moment, in the Western world at least, the path leads to the stinking sewers of anæmic mediocrity, and women are playing an extremely important rôle. Your mother, for instance, has made no advance in understanding, imagination or perception in thirty years. It is perfectly understandable, since it is the nature of her sex. It is only given to men to make an individual pilgrimage, and only a few of them accept the challenge. But she might at least have learned to keep quiet, to be a support to someone, instead of assertively perambulating the world in search of pleasure and flattery, at enormous expense.'

'You can blame me for expense, if you wish,' said Grania, who had turned pale, 'but you can hardly blame me for being a woman.'

'Oh, my God!' The Major rubbed his hand across his eyes. 'That is exactly what I said. If you would only listen, you see. But you are utterly incapable of it.'

'I've been listening,' said Hilda, with passion, 'and I must say I've never *heard* anyone speak . . .'

'Shut up,' said the Major.

'I'm sorry,' he added, 'but really one doesn't have time for these little assertions and protestations of the ego. This is rather important. Try and discover. Try and learn. In Keats's phrase, let the mind be a thoroughfare for all thoughts. These totally unconsidered protections of one's vanity, spoken off the top of the head, are utterly sterile. I don't blame Grania for being a woman, and I don't even blame her for being the sort of woman she is. She is one among millions, and she has capacities beyond them if only she would just once make a little effort. But she won't, you see.'

'Well, I'm sick of men and their selfishness and conceit,' said Grania. 'And I believe Hilda is too. You talk about femininity. Well, it's worth . . .'

'I agree. It's worth everything. But you don't have it, you see. Nor does your friend. And I don't just mean your red breeches. Look at yourselves. There isn't an ounce of femininity left in either of you.'

'I think that's extremely insulting,' said Hilda.

'Perhaps so, but that is of very small importance. Don't worry.

Your number is legion. And since women are losing their femininity, which is all they had to lose, men are losing their virility, for there is little to attract them. That is one of the reasons why Western civilisation is in an advanced state of decay.'

'I think, Father,' said Grania in a trembling voice, 'you're remembering the past. This is something very personal . . .'

'Pah!' said the Major, and he shuddered and hit his pipe hard on the ash-tray beside him. 'I'm sorry, no. I mean, read the *Ladies' Home Journal* if you wish. But keep it to yourself. Don't give us this maudlin drivel.'

'I have *never* read the *Ladies' Home Journal*.'

'I think that's pure nonsense about Western civilisation,' said Hilda. 'I think there's more kindness, now, and more . . .'

'Uhh!' said the Major, shuddering and putting down his book. 'This kind of stuff makes me literally quite sick. I can't describe it to you. A wave of nausea comes right up.'

'Well!' said Hilda.

The Major recovered, swallowing, blinking and giving his head a shake.

'Look,' he said, holding out a forefinger, and using it for emphasis. 'Have a look at modern society, now that you're here. It's easier at this distance, at least I find it so. Just have a look at it. With humility. A highly organised purposelessness. The triumph of materialism. The repetitive working days of an anæmic, conforming, de-personalised race, with tenth-rate entertainment provided to keep the invalids content during their hours of rest.'

'But some of us have to live in it,' said Patrick. 'I do, anyhow.'

'If you do, it can only legitimately be because it is in some way helping you to develop yourself. There's no other justifiable reason.'

'There's money.'

'There is a farm here, of sixty acres.'

'That's funny. Mr Neelan said that on the plane.'

'Did he, indeed? I'm not surprised.'

'But I *have* felt that I was developing. In the past, anyhow.'

'That's all right then.'

'I don't really know what you're talking about,' said Grania. 'But . . '

'In that case, why speak?'

'But it's obvious to me that being alone here you brood on things and . . '

'Oh, God,' said the Major, and he picked up his book again, flushing in the face.

'You won't even get yourself a television set.'

'I think I've explained why,' said the Major, reading his book.

'And for all you say,' continued Grania in a faint voice, 'you don't seem to derive anything from human beings . . .'

'From one per cent of them. Indeed,' added the Major, looking up, 'I don't mind giving you the sentimental satisfaction of knowing that I need someone to communicate with. I'm not a writer, and as one develops one needs to share and test one's discoveries. Unfortunately at my age I find I make advances; an affliction of which most septuagenarians are doubtless free. And I need another mind.'

'Yes, and what happened when *I* invited another mind—that Trinity professor you were always talking about? You went out and weeded your precious lawn, leaving *me* to cope with him. And I was bored stiff.'

'I went out because in your presence adult discussion is utterly impossible. It is interrupted by a persistent stream of female banalities, not to mention a concerted and malicious attempt to prove me a laughable pessimist.'

'Have you asked him since?'

'No. He must have had enough, poor man. And in any case he would appear to be rather more interested in Oriental texts than I am myself.'

'Well, I think deliberately leading a solitary existence in this large and beautiful place is completely absurd,' said Grania.

'You do?'

'Yes. I do.'

'In that case we can proceed to what this discussion is really about.'

The door opened, and Finola was standing there.

'The telephone ma'am,' she said. 'I think it's Mr Sleator.'

'Keep him away from here,' said the Major, as Grania rose and went out. 'It's curious how life always interrupts one's best lines,' he added. 'That's why art is so much more valuable.'

'But what did you mean?' asked Patrick.

'We'd better wait till she returns.'

He crossed the room and poured himself another whisky while Patrick watched him in perplexity and Hilda with fascinated alarm.

He came between them and knocked his pipe out into the fire with the heel of his shoe, and then stood with his back to the fireplace.

'I'm *sorry* I spoke to your mother like that,' he said with concern. 'And to you, too,' he added to Hilda. 'But she is so much more intelligent than she will ever allow herself to be. Once or twice she has opened her mind and genuinely examined what is under discussion. But very rarely.'

'I'm afraid I've rather lost faith in discussions,' said Patrick. 'We used to hold them at Oxford, but . . .'

'It requires a continuing capacity to reach a plane of intellectual joy, which is quite a marvellous experience and also, unfortunately, requires another human being. One finds oneself saying what one never thought one knew. And in turn one hears something which touches an undeveloped part of oneself, and may therefore change one's life. That has happened to me several times.'

Grania came quietly back into the room.

'But I'm afraid people nowadays are destroyed by economics. The working day gives you neither time nor energy for real conversation, for reflection and self-cultivation. . . .'

'That's exactly what strikes me whenever I'm coming back to Ireland,' said Grania.

'Yes, there is still time here,' said the Major, 'but unfortunately the country has other well-organised repressions to make up for it.'

There was a pause.

'That was Dermot,' said Grania, looking at Hilda. 'He has a one-man show opening next week. I knew nothing about it.'

Hilda was no longer capable of replying.

'Well, Father,' said Grania, 'what is it you have to say? I don't think I can take much more.'

'It's quite simple,' he replied, and cleared his throat. 'I'm putting this place up for sale.'

Patrick looked up at him, and so did Grania, turning very pale.

'You're what?' she said.

'It's for sale,' he replied, and put a hand on the mantelpiece.

'You can't mean that,' said Patrick.

'Oh yes, excuse me, I do. To be exact, I've put it on the books of an estate agent, and already your friend Mr Neelan has visited them and expressed great interest. It seems that—of course when the house has been pulled down—the grounds would do very nicely for his next building scheme. We're very lucky, in fact. Houses like this don't normally sell any more. But, who knows, there may be other buyers, and I've been waiting to see you both before actually advertising it in the newspapers.'

'But this is madness, Father,' said Grania.

'On the contrary. It's sanity.'

He went and poured himself another drink.

'We couldn't bear it,' said Patrick.

'No?' said the Major, squirting soda into his glass. 'I wonder if you've any inkling how *I* feel about it.'

'But what's the point?' Patrick insisted.

'Your mother cannot continue to support herself in the way she chooses to live, and I certainly can't. The same is true of your aunt Delia. It is lunacy for me to maintain the place alone. And what is more, I shan't be around much longer and the death duties would leave you nothing.'

Finola struck the gong for dinner out in the hall. They did not hear it.

'But where on earth would you go?' Grania demanded.

'I tinkered with the notion of getting some small place in the West, where people are still alive. But I'm afraid that's rather romantically impossible, since I must earn money. I'll find somewhere hear near the sea. The sea is really the only thing I've missed in this place.'

'Supposing,' said Patrick, 'we stayed and tried to do something here with the farm?'

The Major lit his pipe.

'If you are thinking on those lines, you had better make up your minds pretty quickly.'

'Oh it's all nonsense,' said Grania, and he looked at her with anger and distress. 'I can't believe it. Not Edenmore. *You* sit out there by yourself, weeding and brooding, and brooding and weeding.'

'Listen,' he said, crashing down his glass on the desk. 'While I'm still alive, if *I* am no longer weeding, it will mean that there is no longer any Edenmore!'

Finola struck the gong again, with greater force.

chapter eight

The indicator on the kitchen wall suddenly buzzed, and the light went on beside the words 'Front Hall Door'.

Julia Byrne, who had been bent down, basting the chicken, sprang erect with the spoon in her hand.

'That'll be the priest!' she cried. 'Do you want to leave him out in the cold?'

'No, Julia, I'm going,' said Kathleen. She rushed to a corner chair, on which lay her white apron, tied it around her and straightened her cap.

'God help the man, coming to this house of vice,' said Julia.

Kathleen very nearly fell over Richard, who was lying across the door. She shut him in, remembering the morning's misadventure, and thundered up the steps into the rear hall and through into the front.

When she opened the hall door the whole of Dublin lay stretched out before her: a world of little lights, yellow and red and green, twinkling in the distance in the clear night. Way above there was a full moon. More immediately apparent, however, was the red-veined face of Father Hanna under a black hat.

'Good evening, Father,' she murmured in a voice of awe, carefully curbing her natural exuberance which told her to take him by the hand and shake it heartily.

'Good evening, Kathleen,' he said, stepping in and removing his hat to show a cropped white head. 'And how are you, my child? But I can see for myself—blooming as pretty as ever.'

'Oh, Father,' she replied, turning crimson and reflecting that Paddy had never gone as far as that.

She put the black hat, the black gaberdine mackintosh and his heavy walking-stick on the stand. He was a strongly-built man, decidedly ruddy, with a knobbly nose, odd pock-marks, and penetrating blue eyes. Without his garb he might have been taken for a white-headed, retired boxer who was fond of the bottle. With it, he was beyond all human investigation or remark.

Kathleen tapped on the drawing-room door, heard a voice, opened it, whispered 'Father Hanna' and retired.

The television news-reader was talking extremely loudly, with Tom Neelan and Brendan Smith seated within arm's length of him. Ann Neelan was reading a magazine by the fire. Her mother was rushing towards the priest, crying: 'Tom, will you turn that blessed thing off.'

'No, no, don't let me interrupt,' said Father Hanna. 'We must move with the times. Well, now, you're looking a picture. How d'you keep so young, at all? Tell us, what's the secret?'

'Oh, Father, go along with you!' said Moira, shaking his hand. 'Tom, for the Lord's sake!'

They all hesitated: long enough for the news-reader to say that the self-government clashes had taken place in Africa; the film star had been coshed in her South Kensington mews flat; the bank manager had been shot dead in a bank in Chelsea.

Ann, now standing by the fire, heard the last word and saw artists walking and talking. She was pretty, with black hair and blue eyes in a lively Irish face, wearing a fawn jumper and a green tweed skirt. She had come out with Brendan Smith in his Morris Eight, and was unable to explain why there seemed to be so little to say to him.

Tom switched it off. Without his overcoat, and in his suit, he was less noticeable. The cigarette was still there.

'It's a damn fascinating thing altogether,' he said. 'Though far be it from me, Father, as I need hardly interpolate for a man of your calibre, to regard it as in any way a substitute for the human persona, the community of minds. . . . *Tempora mutantur,* true, true, I'll not deny it. I'd be very foolish if I did. But *nos et mutamur in illis,* that I deny. And I've no doubt whatever that you do too. Enough. A large one, I take it, eh, Father?'

'Ah, not too large, Tom.'

Standing beside the set was a cocktail-cabinet in wood veneer with an electrically-lit top.

Tom poured a large whisky.

'You've met Ann, of course, Father?' said Moira.

'I have, to be sure. Though not as often as I might wish.'

'I'm afraid I've a room in town, Father,' said Ann smiling. 'I live among the evil city-dwellers.'

'Ah, God help us, we're none of us very evil in this old island of ours,' said Father Hanna.

'And you've met Brendan?'

'I have indeed. How's the law? I believe we're to expect great things.'

'Oh, I wouldn't say that, Father,' replied Brendan. He was a quiet young man who was showing individuality in three ways. With his dark blue suit he wore a red knitted tie. A pen and pencil emerged from his top pocket. In his buttonhole was a Pioneer badge.

'Sit by the fire, Father,' said Moira. 'I'm sure you're frozen.'

'Thank you.'

They all sat, and Father Hanna looked about him.

'Every time I call, you know, I can't help thinking what wonders you've done with this place.'

'Oh nonsense, Father,' said Moira.

'I mean it. Not that the previous owners ever welcomed my presence. They were unhappy, faithless people, I'm afraid.'

His eyes moved over the room. The covers and curtains were of pale green silk. It was the same as in Shrewsbury Road, but new. An upright piano in a corner, painted white, gave a touch of modernity to complement the cocktail-cabinet. Over the pink marble mantelpiece hung her portrait my Terence Keogh, who had captured her enigmatically smiling, in an off-the-shoulder ball-dress, her hands with bright red nails folded on her lap. Father Hanna, who was looking at it, said:

'A beautiful piece of work. God gave him a great gift. But he was fortunate in his sitter too.'

'Ah, now, Father,' said Moira, blushing. 'By the way, Father, I'm very much afraid we may have to go in to dinner at any moment, owing to Kathleen being off tonight.'

'Oh, you don't have to explain to me,' he replied, and laughed. 'I know all about it. The rôle of servant and master has undergone a curious change in my lifetime.'

'Something rich and strange, eh,' said Tom, 'the old *tempora mutantur* again.'

'It's no harm, is it?' said Ann, who was sitting opposite the priest.

There was a pause.

'Well, of course, it may be no harm to you, my dear,' said Moira coldly, 'but *I* have to deal with it.'

'There is always the possibility of harm,' said Father Hanna, 'when simple people are presented with temptations. There may even be harm, if you don't mind my saying so, in that machine of yours.'

'Oh quite, quite, Father; to be used with discretion,' Tom agreed, 'the better part of valour.'

'Discretion!' his wife exclaimed. 'I swear to you, Father, he has the thing on morning, noon and night. Rock and rollers and the lot. You can't hear a word they're singing. That England's gone mad, if you ask me. I like to have a chat occasionally, but if I do have a friend coming all the way out here, we can't even speak. And as for all that news and sport, news and sport!'

'One requires to know what the rest of the world is doing. As a man, the Father will support me in that, I have no doubt.'

'I don't see why,' Moira objected. 'All the world's ever doing is fighting. And the men too.'

'I'm by no means uninterested in what the world is doing, I must confess,' said Father Hanna, 'though whether one approves of it or not is another matter.'

He puffed his pipe, and even Tom waited.

'But I greatly fear that this growing interest in alien and un-Christian cultures is extremely dangerous, not of course for our friend Tom here, but for our simple, less well-to-do, and above all younger folk.'

'Aha,' said Tom. 'Now Father, you've spoken the words, as usual. But unfortunately in this respect we shall not remain long in the wilderness.'

'Wilderness?'

'Ah. Correction accepted.' Tom raised his hand. 'No meaning, no offence. Words, words. No, no. What I meant, Father, is that at a not very distant date we are to have our own . . . well, I think you'll have caught my drift, Father?'

'Indeed, there are plans afoot, I believe.'

'*In posse,*' said Tom, 'in potential existence. Let us say no more for the moment except to hope and trust that before very long we shall hear, and see, in our own language, our own folk songs, the pipes, the pipes, the harp that once . . . and so on and so forth.'

'It's a comforting thought, all right,' said Father Hanna.

'Why?' said Ann.

The priest glanced at her.

'But,' he continued, 'we shall need to have faith in our young people. One hopes that they will still prefer the ancient melodies, the jig and reels . . .'

'Oh no doubt of it, Father, no doubt of it. The old values still appertain. In fact, strictly between *entre nous* and no farther than these four walls, I have the greatest confidence that in a few years this country will become once again the spiritual leader of the world.'

'I believe that too, Tom,' said Father Hanna. 'But we must beware of pride.'

'True, true, no doubt. *Vanitas vanitatum.*'

'Ah, it's a great country,' said Moira, 'I wouldn't have any other. Tom's just back from London, you know, Father.'

'So I heard. A great city, for all its faults.'

'You really *are* broad-minded, Father.'

'Well, we must be tolerant. It has its history and tradition. I respect that.'

'And it's alive,' said Ann.

Moira looked at her in surprise. It was becoming impossible to think of her daughter as a lamb, even in her wildest dreams, and although she had not inherited that sparkle, her quiet demeanour was also disappearing. She should never have been sent to a university.

'And what exactly do you mean by that, my dear?' inquired Father Hanna.

'Things are happening over there,' said Ann, flushing. She felt herself unable to think of another word under the priest's pale-eyed stare.

'Now then, now then,' said Tom, also colouring. *'Panem et circenses,* and so on, the Father is not impressed with such matters.'

'Oh, pardon me, Tom, that is not entirely so. Our Church has always paid attention to worldly changes. That is our strength. But I would have thought that things, as our young friend terms them, are happening here too, and there is no better example of it than yourself.'

'Oh, well, far be it from me . . . but since you are kind enough . . .'

'Those aren't the sort of things I mean,' said Ann.

'Don't interrupt your father!' said Moira.

'What on earth *do* you mean?' inquired Brendan, staring at this unknown girl.

'Now, now,' said Father Hanna, 'you young people can argue it out elsewhere. While we're on the subject, tell me, Tom, have you any more plans? I hear the scheme below is going great guns. At any rate, you have me swamped with new parishioners. It will be a relief I can tell you when that new church is built.'

'Oh, it's going to be great, isn't it?' said Moira, defending Tom from his question. 'I pass it on the way in. The Gerratys asked us to lunch today out of the blue, and of course Tom wasn't home yet, so I went.'

'Was that Charlie Gerraty?' asked the priest with sudden interest.

'Yes,' said Moira. The name had a curious effect on her. 'Do you know him, Father?'

'I've met him lately.'

She was about to ask for an opinion, but did not.

'I expect he was full of questions, like me.'

'Well, in a way.'

'He's in the business, of course. *I'm* interested in my parish. Were you thinking of extending, Tom?'

'Well now, between you and me,' said Tom, 'you put me in an awkward situation, as you might say, but trusting in your discretion, I have hopes of buying out Edenmore.'

'You don't say! And is it for sale?'

'In a manner of speaking. It would have to come down, of course, and it depends on the mood of the Major, whom I would very much like to meet by the way. You don't happen to know him?'

'I'm afraid I've never had reason to pay a visit, Tom.'

'You wouldn't,' said Moira.

'You take a severe tone,' said Tom. 'It's a pity *you* never called.'

'Oh, I know them well enough, thank you.'

'I think you might do so now. You were not exactly filled with politesse at the airport. We shall need a new attitude if this is to go through.'

'How much would he want, Tom?'

'Around fifteen thousand, I understand.'

'That's a large sum.'

'Ridiculous, if you ask me,' said Moira.

'It's a lovely old house,' said Ann. 'Would you have to pull it down?'

'I would. It's in the way and the materials are good.'

'Your father is in business, my dear,' said Father Hanna. 'Stones and sentiment don't mix.'

'In England they preserve these old houses,' said Ann.

'Ah, England, England!' Moira exclaimed. 'We've had enough of that, for hundreds of years. Why do you bother about it now? You'd think it was Trinity you went to, not National.'

'Oh, National has little to do with it, Mother, I can tell you that. They're content enough. Aren't they, Brendan?'

Brendan found himself fixed by her flushed and challenging face, and hesitated.

'Except for a few,' she went on. 'The rest will sit around in the Four Courts, or wherever it is, and go to the races, for the rest of their lives.'

'You mean me, I suppose?'

'You and others. You don't want to see anywhere else, do you?'

'I don't, Ann. Why should I?'

'Exactly,' said Moira. 'Why should he? I declare to goodness, Ann, I don't know what's come over you this evening.'

'We're all dead here. We've no idea of anything that's really happening in the world.'

'Oh, we're dead, are we?' said Moira. 'I'm dead, I suppose. And I suppose Father Hanna is dead?'

'Now, then, now then . . .' said Tom. 'The subject on the *tapis*, I think you'll agree with me, Father, is one of the ancient illusions of youth. The far-off hills. . . . Rarely do I quote from the Irish, since I am rarely understood and the Church has fostered an admirable appreciation of Latin, but I quote in translation, "There are long horns on the cows across the water."'

'I don't care how long they are,' said Moira, 'I'm not going to be called dead by my own daughter.'

'I think you should withdraw that, child,' counselled Father Hanna.

'I'm not a child,' said Ann.

Kathleen struck the gong for dinner, out in the hall.

'That's enough now,' said Tom. 'Father was speaking meta-phorically . . . pastorally . . . the shepherd shall guide . . .'

'She knows that perfectly well,' said Moira. 'You'll apologise at once.'

'And I'm not a sheep either. But that's the trouble. We all are. Except for the people who've managed to get out of the country or done a bit of reading. Sartre says . . .'

'I'm a tolerant man,' said Father Hanna, rapping his pipe out on the hearth, 'but I'm not going to hear blasphemy as well.'

Kathleen struck the gong again. She was extremely excited.

chapter nine

Paddy had arrived. The kitchen door was slightly open, and she could hear Julia, with embarrassment, with fear and even this time with anger:

'So there's to be none of that, d'you understand. I've sent them away from here before, and I'll send her away too if there's any of your wickedness. I know you country people . . .'

Kathleen shied off into the small bathroom, just inside the back door, partly to recover from what she had heard and partly to wash her face. It was half filled by the bath, which she thought silly, since in three weeks it had not occurred to her to climb down into it with nothing on, and it certainly played no part in Julia Byrne's scheme of things. For a time it had been handy for washing the Master's shirts, until the Mistress said the collars were done all wrong and sent them to the laundry instead.

She laid her white cap on the end of the bath and placed her spectacles on top of it, and then ran the water in the basin and splashed it on her face. Examining herself in the mirror, she decided that she looked far too healthy and thought of the box of powder and lipstick which she had hidden from Julia under her bed, in the farthest corner, in an old cake-tin whose lid would not fit on properly.

Kathleen paused at the kitchen door, heard: 'Our Blessed Lady is watching you every moment that you're out. Kindly remember that!' and went inside.

Julia Byrne was standing, tall, dark, and mad, Kathleen thought, with her back to the cooker and an egg-whisk in her hand. She was nodding her man's grey head to give emphasis to what she had been saying, and the Sacred Heart on her chest went up and down. Kathleen was nearly in a mood to speak, but the presence of Paddy deterred her. He was seated on a kitchen chair, saying nothing, with Richard lying at his feet. His blue suit and V-necked yellow jersey made him look alarmingly different. Instead of hanging over his eyes, his reddish hair went straight back and was smooth and shiny. She had seen all this at Mass, but that was different. It was seven in the morning, and seen all too vaguely because her eyesight was poor and he kept his distance on account of scandal in the village.

'The Master gave me leave to go,' she murmured.

'Oh, indeed! And who's to bring in the sweet, may I ask?'

'Well, would you ever mind doing it, Julia?'

'I'm the cook. I'm not a house parlourmaid.'

'I know, but just this once. The Master thought you wouldn't mind.'

'I don't know what's got into that Tom Neelan. They should never have moved.'

'And they all seem to be upset or something, so would you ever mind?'

'What do you mean by that, might I ask?'

'Well, Miss Ann has her head down, and Mr Smith's staring at her, and neither of them talking, and the Master's telling the priest the country is to be saved by pigs.'

'I thought as much!'

'The priest ate both breasts of the chicken,' added Kathleen, yielding to the sudden temptation with a relish that astonished her. In the same spirit she said to Paddy, whose presence had provoked it: 'I'll only be a minute,' taking it for granted that the arrangement was accepted.

She opened her bedroom door and Julia shouted:

'That's right. Put on your finery. Let's see your gaudy trinkets. Just wait. She'll come out a proper little Jezebel.'

'That's enough,' said Paddy, and Kathleen went quickly into her room, closed the door softly, and stood for a moment amazed by his daring.

Hearing nothing further, she threw her cap and apron on the

bed, and lay down at full length underneath it, groping with
an outstretched hand for the cake-tin. Her heart was pounding
at the thought of Julia coming in and seeing her two feet pro-
truding from under the bed. She found it. The ill-fitting lid
clattered off on to the floor, and she instinctively drew in her
feet so that she was completely hidden, but no one came.

A moment later she had put on the powder quite freely, since
in the heat of battle her face had turned scarlet, and the lipstick
very faintly. The mirror stood on a dressing-table, and above it
hung a Christmas calendar five years old on which Our Lady
smiled down at the Holy Child. As she put on her frock she
hummed, slightly wrong, 'Some Enchanted Evening', until she
heard herself doing it. The frock was black, with large red roses
on it, and bought especially for the occasion, with six weeks'
wages, in Lee's of Rathmines.

When it was on, it gave her some slight sense that she was
competing. She was accustomed to Paddy when he was dressed
for milking the cows, whose mooing had dispatched so many,
or feeding the pigs, or, lately, bringing in the harvest. The latter
had been a terrible affair, done with unknown women from the
village; which she had done so vigorously at Kilsheelan, and now
could not do, imprisoned in cap and apron in the house. But the
unknown women did not have him standing about when they
hung out the Master's socks on the line in the vegetable garden,
looking shy and admiring.

She added a black coat and black shoes, pulled on white gloves,
picked up a black shiny handbag, which was also new from Lee's,
and was ready. She polished her spectacles with a corner of the
dressing-table cloth, placed them on her nose and wondered if
she could now really be called Jezebel. She took another comforting look at Our Lady, and everything was so successful that
she grasped the tin, bent down, and almost casually slid it under
the bed so that it clanked against the far wall.

Fortunately no criticism was offered. Julia had turned away to
the cooker and was doing something to the apple charlotte.

Paddy had opened the door. Kathleen bent towards Richard's expectant brown eyes and open laughing mouth and said: 'Good night, Richard love.' He was coming out with them, and she said: 'No, no, Richard. You stay here with Julia.' The dog looked thunderstruck. Paddy quickly closed the door on him, and there was a yelp and an exclamation from Julia.

'That was lucky. She wasn't looking,' said Kathleen. She suddenly felt like giggling.

'I told her to say nothing when you came out.'

This new man was great.

They went past the bathroom through the rear door and down the narrow way between the garage and the house, and were out in front, with Dublin below them. It was cold. She said:

'Did you not bring a coat?'

'I don't need one.'

The full moon was up above, but there was only one star, near to it in the blackness. A light shone in one of the few windows of the Murrough-Bryants' that emerged from the deeper darkness of the trees, and she thought of her sister, Finola, getting ready, though not in that upper room but in the basement. Beyond were the lights of the capital, with the odd, red light from some cinema, the yellowing flashing beam of the airport on the horizon, coming round regularly like that of a lighthouse, and the long row of orange lights that followed the coast road, round in a semicircle, out towards Howth.

Going down the drive, under the tall trees, they were in darkness. It was silent, except for the crunching noise that their feet made on the peculiar ashes that Mr Neelan had put down. She felt exhilarated. She was away from Julia Byrne, and it had begun. There was plenty of time, too, owing to the Master letting her off early. The bus would not even have come up the hill yet.

'I *am* thrilled, Paddy,' she said.

She could not see him in the dark.

'Why would you be that?'

'Oh, I don't know. Everything.'

'You're a goof.'

About ten paces farther on something strange and exciting and quite new to her made her stop.

'What's up?'

'Nothing,' she said.

Yet almost at once she found that she had held out her arms and placed them around him, and that they were kissing each other; which they had not done before.

When it seemed to have become nearly wicked she stepped away from him. Her spectacles felt as if they were falling off her nose and she straightened them. She was filled with embarrassment and shame, and intensely happy.

'Am I gone crazy or what?' she said, and laughed.

She thought he would never answer. But then he said: 'You're not crazy at all,' in a curious voice.

She turned and walked on, and their feet crunched on the gravel.

She had made a wonderful and frightening discovery. Previously, marrying him and keeping chickens had really been a dream. Now it appeared perfectly possible, and this was alarming. She tried to think of something else.

'Finola says you're very thick these days with this Mick that's coming along.'

'He's a bright lad all right.'

'I never spoke to him. The only few times Finola had me there was in the house, in her room. I was never in the gate lodge.'

Paddy laughed quite loudly in the silence, which was odd.

'Mick probably wouldn't have been there. He's in town most of the time. I only see him on a Saturday or Sunday.'

'I've seen him on Sundays, with his father and you at Mass; a long way off. And you never come near me after.'

'It's better so.'

This seemed to confirm what had just happened, and left her silent. When were they to admit it to everyone? Tomorrow?

Paddy said, almost laughing again:

'You haven't seen him often at Mass. He's not very regular.'

'That's nothing to be proud of.'

It was an unsatisfactory moment for disagreement. The drive had mounted up to the road, and they were out of the gates, at the top of the village. The bus stop was still higher up the road, beside the hedge, where there were two cottages, one of them being the post office and the end of the village.

The only illumination came from these cottages, but there was now a faint and eerie moonlight that made the sweet-papers and general accumulation of litter shine forth on the black road outside the post office. A few figures could be dimly seen, waiting for the bus. They talked in soft voices, awed by the night and the moon. Paddy recognised them, but Kathleen did not. She was still a stranger here.

'You must miss not having your own father and mother to go with?'

'Where?'

'To Mass, I mean.'

'Ah, they've been dead a good few years, God rest them.'

'And what does Mick's father think of him working in town and not in the gardens?'

'Oh, the old boy. He's out of date. Mick doesn't fancy pulling up weeds by the hour.'

'And I suppose *you're* out of date, working on the farm?'

'So Mick says,' he replied after a pause.

'Well, I never!'

This was very confusing. She only knew that she was not going to like Mick.

'He's going to England, I believe,' said Paddy.

'England!'

'Yeh.'

'What ever for, in the name of goodness?'

'He has friends. In Liverpool. He says they know how to live over there. They're up to date.'

'Gracious, I never heard such nonsense. And what's wrong with it here?'

'It's quiet,' said Paddy. The bus had been rumbling up the hill, and now turned the corner, a roaring face with shining eyes that illuminated the whispering groups and removed all awe from the scene. It turned into a side road, backed out of it with another roar, and came down the hill again to rest at the stop. It was a green single-decker, liberally spattered with mud and further camouflaged by its windows which were grey with human breath. The small company that had made the full journey from town descended, and there were greetings between them and those about to climb in. A fat, smiling woman said to Paddy: 'And where are *you* gallivanting off to at this hour of the night?' She kept on looking at Kathleen, who took a dislike to her.

They were the last to mount, and Kathleen was glad to note that the other five had all gone up to the front. They chose the seats at the back, so that when Finola and Mick got on they would sit facing them. The five looked elderly and comfortable, and were now whispering again, as everyone sat patiently on the green leather seats under the two bright, naked electric light bulbs. The conductor had gone round to stand with the driver by the bonnet and smoke cigarettes.

Although Kathleen was aware that something tremendous had happened to her, it was not something that she could speak about, and although she knew suddenly that she wanted to hold his hand on the seat, she could not do that either. She sat wishing to goodness they would hurry up. The bus was warm, and contained a pungent human odour of which she was unaware, and it was undoubtedly quiet at the moment.

She said: 'I bet it's not quiet at the ballroom,' and smiled at him.

He smiled too, but did not turn to look at her. 'I shouldn't think so. I'm no dancer, I warn you.'

'Ah sure, I'm not either. But what does it matter? It'll be gas.'

He seemed distant and unwilling to face her. Perhaps she had really made a mistake; or perhaps it was just being spotted by the fat woman.

'Mick speaks very highly of the band. It's from Liverpool.'

'Oh.'

The conductor came walking round, threw his cigarette on the grass bank where it glowed red in the dark, climbed in and gave the bell a bang. The driver started the engine and the whole bus trembled, and moved away.

Kathleen turned and rubbed some of the breath off the window between them with her white-gloved hand. She knew that it was the wrong thing to do, but being housebound in cap and apron she had only seen the village three times in her life. It ran down the hill from the Neelans' gate very nearly to the gate of the Murrough-Bryants. It consisted of low, grey, Victorian cottages, in one of which Paddy had lived with friends since his father died; and then the church and Father Hanna's big grey house, both set back behind trees, and two public houses. The latter dominated the scene at night. They both had a custom sufficiently well established, and a geography sufficiently remote, to have survived the Intoxicating Liquor Act of 1960, which put an end to the 'bona fide' and thus aimed a blow at the outer structure of the capital's social life. Cars still came hurrying out of town and, much later, went weaving back again.

The bus passed O'Sullivan's, on the right. The sign was in red neon, up on the first and top storey, looking brilliant against the grey. It catered largely for the 'locals' and was modest, but Cullen's, which presented itself at the bottom of the hill on the left, was not. It was a huge, rambling place, which had constantly extended itself in relation to increasing late-night custom from Dublin. Not only was 'Cullen's' in red neon, but also 'saloon bar,' 'public bar' and 'lounge'. Next door to it, Mr Cullen had excavated almost an entire field as a concrete car park. It was no mere gesture. Tonight it was filled with cars. A noisy crowd of young people had just got out of a Volkswagen. Kathleen heard one girl calling back to another: 'Did you bring the cigs, Maureen?'

'Will you look at the cars!' she said. 'They must be well off. D'you ever go there?'

'Not much.'

'Ah go on, I bet you do.'

'I've been once or twice. It's a haunt of Mick's, when he's home. There he is now, the old chancer!'

Through the fog on the opposite window she could just see the two figures waiting outside the Murrough-Bryants' gate. Then they climbed aboard and sat across the way, and for a while she was filled with confusion and surprise.

She had not seen her sister since they went together to the Spanish dancers at the Olympia and for some reason all through the second half Finola had suffered from hiccoughs. She looked alarmingly 'done up' since that occasion. Her full mouth was scarlet, and she had put peculiar black lines under her lively eyes. She wore a bright red coat over a bright green dress, neither of which Kathleen had seen before. Of course, as Kathleen now remembered, she had left the Neelans for much higher wages and perhaps a much higher style of life. She was bristling and in a temper, curiously enough, and Kathleen could not quite make out what it was all about.

The reason for her difficulty was that her attention was distracted by the extraordinary creature at Finola's side. He was thin and pale, with black, greasy hair that came down beside his ears in side-whiskers. Over his spiky nose and hollow cheeks were bright little eyes that glanced about all the time and had settled on her for an instant as he sat down, in a knowing way. He was chewing very quickly at one corner of his mouth, but she could not see what he was chewing. He wore a peculiar black suit with the coat too long for him, and instead of a tie what looked like a black bootlace.

Finola was still going on about whatever it was, and Kathleen tried to follow.

'Oh yes, I head it distinctly,' she said, tossing her head. 'The servants are all manure, he sez.'

'Hah,' said Mick, and for a second Kathleen thought that he had spat out whatever was in his mouth. But he went on chewing again. Then he smiled in a funny way at Paddy, and said:

'Farmer boy would think it a flippin' compliment, eh?'

Paddy laughed!

'What do you mean, you old chancer? It makes things grow, I suppose.'

'Sure. Sure, sure.' (He was talking American.) 'Himself and the rest grow out of us.'

'What an idea!' exclaimed Finola. 'Disgusting. The nerve o' them!'

'Well, they're not gonna grow out o' me.'

'Are you still set on Liverpool, Mick?'

'*Am* I. Boy!'

Kathleen supposed he meant 'yes'. He was looking suddenly down to the front of the bus, as if for more company, and had begun clicking his thumb and finger in a nervy way and in an even rhythm, as if he heard music playing. Then he turned back to them.

'They'll be takin' me off on a flippin' cart. Even the manure's leavin' the bloody country, they'll say. Though maybe not to Oxford. The dear old bloody varsity, eh what? Patrick Price-Jones, my deah.'

'I heard he was back,' said Paddy, chuckling.

'I don't know what you're talking about,' said Finola, 'but I know we don't have to be *servants* over there. Nor manure either. My God, what a crew! That Mr Flanagan as I'm supposed to call him. Mrs would be more like it. Or Miss.'

'Oh, don't be unkind, dear,' said Mick to Finola in such a peculiar way that it put her into a good temper all of a sudden. Paddy, too, was grinning; and Kathleen tried to smile.

'He's good with cars, mind you,' said Mick, changing his expression at once and looking in a dreamy way down the bus as if he had forgotten them all again.

'I wouldn't be surprised,' said Finola, working herself up once more. 'And that Mary Cullen. On and on about the "gentry". On and *on*. She's been with them fifteen years, and before that it was more "gentry" out at Howth.'

'She's what they used to call the old retainer, my deah,' said Mick. 'All the bloody gentry have them, but they're nearly finished.'

'Which?' said Finola. 'Which do you mean are finished?'

'Both. Both. Both,' replied Mick, clicking his fingers as if it was a tune.

He alarmed Kathleen, and his language made her blush, but Paddy must have noticed that she was sitting there silent.

'Julia Byrne's been with *my* people twenty years,' she said.

'Well, *they're* not gentry, my dear,' said Finola. 'Don't kid yourself.'

'Trying hard,' said Mick. 'They're the worst.'

'You should *hear* Mary Cullen on the Neelans,' said Finola. 'It's the only thing we agree on.'

The bus had passed the Neelan housing estate. It was nearly full now, and the lights of town were shining, red and yellow, through the foggy windows.

'Julia Byrne says they're sinful,' Kathleen volunteered. 'But I don't know what she's talking about half the time.'

'The old bag,' said Mick, looking down the bus.

'D'you know her?' Kathleen addressed him directly for the first time.

'I've told him about her,' said Paddy.

They were quiet. A huge red-faced man had seated himself on the aisle, with a brown paper parcel in his lap, and was repeating every so often: 'God save the King!'

'The King is himself,' Paddy murmured in her ear. 'It used to cause trouble, but nearly everyone knows it now.'

'Gracious!'

'So they're still writing for you to go over, are they?' he asked Mick.

'Yeh, I'd a scrawl from Peter Clancy. He's making good money on a buildin' scheme. But I'm not sure that's for me.'

'I shouldn't think so.'

'Are you getting at me, boy?'

'No, no.'

'I'll tell you one thing. When I get over there'll be none of that whingin'. Half the time he seems to want to be back. But for the money. You'd want an Irish crowd to have a bit o' sport, he says. As if there wasn't one there. Getting together and singing songs of home. I can tell you there'll be none of that from me.'

'Would you not write to your father?' asked Kathleen, with daring.

'I'm not a great one with the pen,' he said, winking at Finola so that she giggled again.

'Tch, tch, tch,' said the old conductor, who had been listening.

'What's wrong with you, Grandpa?'

'Tch, tch,' he repeated, giving Mick a long and unpleasant look, and he turned away and busied himself with his tickets.

'Old bag,' said Mick.

'What'll you do, then?' asked Paddy.

'I dunno. I'm going to talk to the boys in the band tonight. I hear they're a great little combo.'

'A what?' asked Kathleen.

'Combo. Combo. Combo,' he replied, clicking his fingers.

Suddenly she saw her ageing father standing at the gate, awaiting the annual visit of the combine harvester. He was small and wiry, with hollow cheeks and a few teeth. Behind him the fields were golden. Up the dusty road in the sunshine came the great red monster. In the little grey house her mother, who was younger and strong, was baking bread for all the helpers, and was being helped herself, in a sort of way, by the youngest sister, Deirdre, who was a bit soft in the head. Out in the fields their one and only brother, Martin, wonderful Martin, was giving instructions to the men and women who had come for the day. They had lost two daughters within a few months, and she wondered how they were managing now. It was all her mother's idea, for their own good. There was small hope of finding a man in Kilsheelan, and she was already twenty-five, and Finola twenty-four. Maybe it was all a mistake, she thought, and then she remembered the man beside her and glanced at him. No, it had not been a mistake.

'Here we are,' said Paddy.

The bus was drawing up at Burgh Quay.

They rose, and were first to descend, and Kathleen's excitement returned with the sudden impact of the city at night. She put a hand on the rounded cold top of the low wall beside her and glanced over, down to the low muddy waters of the Liffey. Red and yellow lights were reflected there, with swans drifting quietly about between them.

'Come on,' said Paddy.

She turned and saw that Finola and Mick had already gone on ahead. The Manhattan Ballroom was only up at the end of O'Connell Street, so she presumed they were walking.

There were crowds moving in both directions and staring in the bright shop windows, and she put her hand under his arm in order not to lose him. He did not seem to flinch.

It was tremendous after the mountains. The wide street was roaring with traffic. The statues in the middle looked very grand and imposing. All the way there seemed to be bright and shiny milk-bars, in several of which there were young people looking rather like Mick Trench.

'What do you thing of him?' asked Paddy.

'What?'

'Of Mick.'

'Well, I dunno. I don't think I ever really saw anyone like him. He's a bit peculiar, d'you know what I mean?'

'Ha, ha. You'll get used to him. He's bright.'

'Oh, he is. It's only . . . I dunno.'

'Heggal or *Mail* or *Press,'* a newspaper-man was shouting. The windows of Clery's were bright and gay, with thick flannel nighties and nearly everything else priced at 9/11d. The Metropole was showing *The Lady's in Love* and the Carlton *Western Guns.* They came up on Finola and Mick, who was saying something about the Savoy, which was having a world première that very night of an American musical, *Father Pat.* There was a crowd outside, with children and old women in rags in the front row, watching the cars disgorging the people in evening dress.

She suddenly recognised a woman in a black ball-dress, gingerly crossing the street, with a handsome man in a dinner-jacket beside her. These two, however, were not going to the Savoy but to the Gresham Hotel next door.

'Gracious!' Kathleen exclaimed. 'That lady's a friend of the mistress. It's Mrs Gerraty.'

'I've heard of him,' said Mick. 'Son of the famous Seamus. *There's* a film for you. The Gerraty Story . . . our fight for freedom, now shooting at Ardmore Studios.'

'Pardon?' said Kathleen.

'I didn't care for her dress,' said Finola, as the couple disappeared inside the hotel.

They walked on, in pairs, and began to climb the hill where the Gate Theatre and Groome's hotel were face to face. Above was the noble square; the city's north side; the tall, grand, Georgian houses, once the homes of their foreign rulers. There seemed to be so many dance-halls that Kathleen thought she would never have found the Manhattan alone. It was only indicated by a flickering red sign in one of the elegant first-floor windows. Up on the steps there were about twenty young men, and she wondered why they were not going in. Several of them looked at Finola in a strange way and one of them whistled. There were more of them cluttering up the narrow hallway inside, where a rough-looking man was sitting behind a trestle table selling tickets. Kathleen could now hear the exciting thumping of the band and the whine of a saxophone. Paddy was paying. Mick was talking to two of the men who looked alarmingly like himself. They both had side-whiskers and one of them was chewing. Finola was settling her hair, and did not seem a bit put out.

Paddy led them on into a big room where the sound of the band was very loud. She could not see it for a moment, because once again the doorway was filled with young men. These were making a lot of noise, laughing loudly and pretending to punch each other, and she found them rather frightening. Then she saw the band of five men in white coats—though not very white—up on a dais at the end behind a notice saying: 'Jimmy Griffin and his Four Aces.' The wall rose high behind them to a cornice with a complicated design. The band was in full swing, but there was no one on the floor. Seated on benches down either side of the great room were girls in pretty frocks.

'You can leave your coats down there,' said Paddy.

They had to walk across the dance-floor, down to a room at the end beside the band. Finola went ahead. Kathleen felt all the girls watching them.

It was a small, empty room full of coats.

'Why aren't they dancing?' whispered Kathleen as they took off their coats.

'It's always the same,' said Finola. 'It's no country for girls.' She put her head round somebody's collar and added: 'That's a good-looker of yours.'

Kathleen was astonished, more by the 'yours' than by anything else. She had not imagined herself as being in possession.

But then maybe she was.

Certainly, she was suddenly excited at the prospect of dancing with him.

Her dress had climbed up on her and she was delayed a while, pulling it down over her hips. On coming out she saw Finola going up to Paddy, who was standing on the near side of the group at the door. Several girls were now being invited to dance, and she was both surprised and alarmed to see Finola and Paddy going forward when Mick gripped her by one hand and flung her across the room.

That, at least, was what it felt like, and she uttered a shout. But already he had seized her other hand and hurled her away in the opposite direction.

She turned right round, having no choice, and faced him again.

He seemed to have gone out of his mind. His black eyes were staring. He was chewing fiercely to the rhythm of the band. He was clapping his hands and commending: 'Give, sister, give!'

'Give what?' she cried.

But he gripped her hand again, and once more forced her to turn in a circle.

'That's it, baby, that's it,' he said.

And slowly she realised that this turning was what she was supposed to be doing. It was really quite easy once you knew. She had imagined that it was going to be the jigs and reels or the old waltzes that you heard from Radio Eireann, but this was good too. Kathleen had a great capacity for enjoyment.

She spun, when requested, noting that he himself appeared to be doing nothing, and was very pleased indeed when he shouted:

'You're quite a kid!'

She wondered if Paddy had seen her and whether he was impressed or horrified, and she was already so adept at this exhilarating performance that she was able to look about her.

He was dancing in his usual, careful way with Finola. They were talking, and for an instant she was a little hurt that Paddy had not been keeping his eye on her, especially with all that shouting.

But they seemed to be having fun too, and that was the important thing.

chapter ten

Patrick walked down the drive, which was dark because the tall rhododendrons obliterated the moonlight. The Major had read a book through dinner and then retired to bed, and his mother and Hilda, having exhausted all topics that did not concern Edenmore, were now playing Scrabble. The events of the day, culminating in his grandfather's astonishing ultimatum, had been most bewildering. It was extremely difficult to accept that only this morning he had woken up with a hang-over in his mother's flat in Knightsbridge.

A light shone from the gate lodge. He had already been greeted by Trench when he made his tour of the grounds. He wondered if he was seated there alone or with his terrible son, Mick. It would be interesting to see inside, but he thought it better not to intrude. He had not done so since he was a small boy. He remembered a huge chest-of-drawers and a clutter of Mrs Trench's religious and Victorian ornaments. Her heavy muslin curtains were still in the window and he could see nothing through them.

Out on the road there was moonlight and a tall black bramble hedge. It was very still and rather cold. A couple stood together against the hedge, whispering. He began to walk up the hill. He had been impressed and humbled by his grandfather's fire which now, in his seventies, drove him in pursuit of quality as forty years ago it had driven him over walls and gates. He, on the other hand, seemed to accept everyone. Even Mr Neelan was not entirely a screaming bore, nor Hilda entirely insane. He was too 'understanding', and not ambitious enough. There was sufficient tolerance about nowadays. One should be disturbed, or at least have feelings and express them without restraint. His mother had said at dinner that 'dear Hugo' Lorrimer would never forgive her if she was not at the opening of *The Kiss of Death* next week. It was on the same day as Dermot Sleator's show, and by a new young playwright who was spoken of as the Tennessee Williams of Manchester. He had said that he would not be there. Perhaps he was envious. At any rate, it was foolishly stubborn of him.

The huge car park was filled with cars, most of them extremely dirty. There were Volkswagens, Borgwards, Mercedes, Dauphines and Fiats, presenting a Continental air that removed England still farther off. On the redly illuminated concrete expanse in front three small girls were playing tag. The eldest halted, seeing him, and inquired: 'Have yeh the time, misther?' He replied: 'Yes, it's just nine,' and was surprised to see a man emerge from Cullen's and reel across the concrete and through the grey entrance of the Gents. The girls watched him and, glancing at Patrick, put their hands to their mouths to suppress their snorts of laughter. Then they began to chase each other again.

Patrick opened the door of the Saloon Bar, and was again surprised because the silent, moonlit night had yielded up about one hundred people engaged in thunderous conversation. Men in mackintoshes, a number of them wearing hats, sat on chromium stools the full length of the long bar. Green leather benches and chairs, with yellow-topped tables, occupied the rest of the expanse. Along the wall above the benches was a 'modern' fresco symbolising Dublin, chiefly in terms of ill-drawn Liffey bridges and shawlies selling flowers. It was lit from above by concealed lighting. Below it, there were ten or so women among the assembly of men, and wherever they were seated there were continual shrieks of laughter. But a much more intense flirtation was proceeding at the bar, where the men sat face to face and back to back, whispering, confiding and nodding, with mutual love in their eyes, and profound content at being away from women, mundanity and responsibility, and approaching the Truth in a growing stupor. They seized each other's elbows and rapped each other's chests, and the din caused by their combined confidences was astonishing.

He found a narrow space at the bar between two of them, who politely broke away, but appeared oblivious of him as he ordered a large Irish.

'It came as a bloody awful shock to your man, I need hardly say.'

'My God, I can imagine.'

'But between you and me and the gatepost, all had not been a bed of roses in that particular relationship for a bloody long time.'

'Is that right?'

'There's been no love lost between them for a year or more.'

'Well, well, so it's divorce, eh?'

'That's about it, Jack.'

'Too bad. Ah, well.'

'Not a bloody horse left. Himself has taken away the lot.'

'When owner and trainer disagree.'

'Mind you, he was a bloody good trainer once.'

'Oh, by God, he was.'

Patrick's suede shoes were sticking to some liquid on the linoleum. He stepped back and moved over towards the tables. He had suddenly recalled that an advertising colleague had offered him a small but elegant villa at St Tropez, in which to relax in the warm October sunshine. This was different. At one of the tables there were two dark-haired, lively rather than pretty, over-dressed girls who sat together against the wall, with two men opposite them. There had been much laughter here. The table was covered with bottles and glasses.

'What did you do with the cigs, Maureen?'

'Ah God, Nuala, you're like a jack-in-the-box. You had them a minute ago.'

'Well, they're gone now,' said Nuala, looking about her. 'Honest to God, *pipe smokers!*'

Both men were indeed smoking pipes, and they were very similar. They were both in their thirties and rather plump, in new check coats and fawn trousers. One had laid a new check cap down among the bottles. They had perhaps been to Baldoyle races. They were possibly stockbrokers or accountants; at any rate, newly prosperous Dubliners.

One of the men ordered cigarettes from a serving-boy in a white coat, who looked to be aged about ten.

'You're an expensive pair,' he said to the girls.

'None of your lip now, Joe Slavin!' Maureen replied.

'That reminds me of a story,' he said, lowering his voice and murmuring to the other man, who laughed.

'Well, let us in on it,' said Maureen, 'for heaven's sakes, man.'

He hesitated, and then murmured across the table.

There were shrieks.

'Oh, that's awful! I'll tell Father Conlan on you.'

'I think the Father might appreciate the story.'

'I doubt it very much,' said Nuala, and she glanced at Maureen and they were overcome again.

Patrick noted now that a man at his table had been gazing at him with the native expression of total intimacy, which was both flattering and unnerving. 'Present me, not with the details of your life, but with your true persona, and I'll present you with mine.' It was a young man of about twenty-five, poorly dressed, with hollow cheeks, an individual peasant-like face, and the sad and familiar absence of all his teeth save the ones in front.

'Were you at the match?' he asked.

'No. No, I wasn't,' Patrick replied. 'Where was that?'

'Dalymount Park. I expect it'd be the rugby you'd go to in any case,' said the man with a smile.

'Well, yes, I suppose it would.'

'I'm on my way back, as a matter a' fact.'

'Oh. Back where?'

'London.'

'Really? What are you doing there?'

'Travelling.' He stubbed out his cigarette. 'It's interesting, mind you.'

'In what way?'

Evidently satisfied by the encounter, the man placed an elbow on the table and leaned across.

'Because it deals with people, you see, as individuals. It's the same as trade, really, only more so. It's really one individual appealing to another individual, and there's nothing more interesting than that, is there?'

'Perhaps not.'

'Furthermore I like to meet as many different kinds of people as possible, with different ideas. I like to hold arguments.'

'You do?'

'I've just been home, you know. Kerry. And God it's like beating your head against a stone wall. They'll never learn. The people were rich on onions, you see. I know, because my father's the main shopkeeper. Then of course came the blight. Well, it's all agin' the government, agin' the government. The country should be like Denmark, like Holland, agricultural, efficient, and if it isn't, blame the government. Well, what happens in this case, the government sends down a demonstrator to show how they do the onions in Holland. I was *most impressed*. You don't have the big ditch. You have this special kind of American plough which only costs five pounds. A lovely job. Twenty people from the whole town turned out for that demonstration!'

He leaned back, by way of emphasis.

'Really?'

He came forward again.

'And a man on the wall said to me: "The old methods are good enough." And yet they were happy before and well off when the onions were right. My God, it'll be a damn good thing when that television covers the country and they all feel the need of washing-machines and so on.'

'Do you honestly think so?'

'Most definitely I do. It'll buck them up. Make them see sense. As it is the country's dead. God, I'm glad to be going back. Ah well, I've got to be off now. Pack the bags and so on.'

'Give my regards to London.'

'I will that. Will you be over yourself?'

'I'm not quite sure.'

'You'd be better off, believe *you* me. Good night, so.'

'Good night.'

Patrick sat looking on the company in sudden depression, wondering what had brought this man on a lone pilgrimage out to Cullen's. Its reputation must be high. However, in spite of having been served with another drink by the small boy, he was weary of the place. He decided to go and have a look at O'Sullivan's.

When he came out, the night seemed twice as cold. The three girls had gone. He had not put on an overcoat and was conscious that his clothes were going to be conspicuous up the hill. But appearances mattered less here than in England.

The light from the Neelans' sitting-room was now visible high up in the darkness. It gave him a homely impression of contented middle-class security, since he was unaware that a family evening of almost comparable tension had been proceeding there. He reflected that millions of such people in Ireland—a vast majority—never entered a public house, whereas for him it was the entrée to the Irish in their greatest variety, and therefore what occurred there tended in his eyes to be representative. He remembered a few occasions on which he had seen the Major in a pub. His grandfather altered and was forthcoming. He always chatted with the publican, and said 'aye' for yes, because that was the way one talked to the people, consumed his one drink rapidly, and went on his way, presumably leaving behind a memory of old-world courtesy and a gentleman in need of a quick refresher before galloping on.

And now Edenmore was to go unless . . . It was incredible. He found it quite impossible to comprehend.

Tonight the Major had seemed more like a father than the true holder of that position, Reggie Price-Jones, a kindly person but a stranger, now drinking heavily in a cottage in Berkshire, part of the remains of family property. His mother was attracted to weak men. His stepfather, Tony Agerton-Willy, divorced in the spring, resembled his father very closely, except that he still survived in London, with the help of the Stock Exchange. He wondered if Count André was similar.

The village was now running down either side of the hill: the grey Victorian cottages, the church, and Father Hanna's grey house back behind the trees, with no lights on tonight. The red neon sign announced O'Sullivan's and illuminated a television aerial attached to the chimney above. It was a confusing announcement because the pub was really O'Toole's. When O'Sullivan died his widow, formerly an O'Toole from Cork, was too heavy and arthritic to continue on her own, and her brother had sold his own pub in Cork and come to run hers.

In a small porch, especially built on to the front to prevent inebriates from falling directly under cars rushing down the hill, Patrick was faced by two brown doors. He chose the one to the left. The room that he entered was deserted because it was the smart part, for ladies or local gentry or the few Dubliners who ignored Mr Cullen's beguiling lights and came up the hill. It was divided from the neighbouring room by a brown wooden partition running up to the counter. The other room evidently was popular tonight because it was very noisy. Curiously, the smart room was otherwise identical, with brown walls and brown wooden benches against them. Irish 'contemporary' was Mr Cullen's prerogative in this area.

Mr O'Toole stood behind the counter, and a very dirty old man sat on a stool with his back to the partition, smoking a crude pipe. Mr O'Toole wore a dark red jersey and had his shirt-sleeves pulled up to the elbows, showing powerful forearms. He was dipping glasses in water and drying them. He was tall and thickset. He had greyish hair, very neatly brushed, and a most expressive face with a rather pointed nose and chin. He had been the same for ten years and his age was impossible to determine.

'Well, look what's arrived,' he said and stopped wiping a glass. 'Look what's arrived. Hallo, stranger.'

'You remember me, Mr O'Toole?'

'Oh, ho, I do indeed! "Remember me", he says. And why wouldn't I remember you?'

His voice was curiously loud, and went up and down and then up at the end, in the Cork accent. He savoured his words, particularly the long ones, in an attractive way.

'Patrick Price-Jones. From Edenmore. Is it not?'

The bar ran on into the other room, and this must have been audible even through the hubbub there. The old man with the pipe turned a quiet eye on Patrick, unexcited by Mr O'Toole's gift for emphasis.

'That it,' said Patrick.

'You're taller.'

'Am I?'

'You are. And tell us, how has the world been treating you all these years?'

(Patrick might have been deaf.)

'Oh, well enough, thanks.'

'You're married, I suppose?' Mr O'Toole winked, while wiping the glasses again.

'No. And yourself?'

'Me, is it? God bless us. Not likely! And what is your order? I've got a nice dry wine, but none of them drink it here, I need hardly tell you.'

'I think I'd really rather have a large Irish. What about yourself, Mr O'Toole?'

'Lord no. I never touch anything. Nor do I smoke. *Your* memory's not so good.'

'How do you survive?'

'Survive, is it? Oh, I survive all right. I survive all right.'

'You do indeed. I must say you look exactly the same.'

'Oh, compliments now, is it!'

As he turned to pour the drink his expression entirely altered. He frowned in concentration and his jawbones were moving as if he were tense. But he was himself when he came forward again;

a warm and considerable personality. Only the voice seemed not wholly sympathetic, being directed, as it were, to someone else away out in the fields. Perhaps it was merely a countryman's habit.

'And from where have you arrived, to honour us with a visit? London, is it?'

He was leaning on the counter on his left arm, fingering a bottle-top in his right hand.

'Yes, but I've just left my job.'

'Lord save us. You don't say. And what was it?'

'Advertising.'

'Well now. My goodness. We're getting plenty of that these days—from Belfast.'

'I saw you've television.'

'We have indeed. We're not entirely in the backwoods here, you know. We're *up to date*. Though I prefer to read myself. Have you read this *Lolita?*'

'Well . . . some of it.'

' "Some of it," he says, I'd better ask you no more. We had a writer here the other night.'

'Really?'

'What do you think of that now? O'Sullivan's is looking up, you'll be saying. An American. A most intelligent and agreeable fellow he was too. A *novelist*. Harry C. Rodgers.'

'Oh.'

'Harry C. Rodgers. He wrote it out for me. I have it in my wallet. If I had my coat I'd show it to you.'

'That was very nice.'

'T'was so. Very nice indeed. I was delighted. Ah well . . . well, well . . . and what will you do now? You're not intending to remain here, are you—with us *provincials?*'

'I don't really know yet. Why do you call yourself that?'

'Well, 'tis what we are, isn't it? My God, sure what else are we?'

'Well, you're . . .'

'You see, you haven't an answer. You're *tongue-tied*. Ah, sure 'tis no harm. We can't all be *Londoners,* can we?'

'No.'

He gazed at the bottle-top in his hand for a while. Then he suddenly threw it away into a bin, and said: 'Well, I'm neglecting my other customers. You mustn't *monopolise* me, as they say. If you'll excuse me.'

'Of course.'

Curiously, it did seem abrupt; as if Mr O'Toole had not been at all interested.

The other gentleman was also enigmatic, in his own way: silence.

'That's a lovely night,' Patrick remarked.

The man stared ahead. He took out his pipe. 'Ahem,' he said, and reinserted it.

'A full moon,' said Patrick.

No answer.

'Do you live in the village?'

The gentleman obviously was stone deaf. This must be why he was not tempted by the sounds of revelry next door. Embarrassed, Patrick retreated out into the porch, and through the right-hand door.

This time there was scarcely room to stand. In a very small space at least twenty men of toothless, hollow-cheeked aspect, in shabby old overcoats, were having an extremely merry evening. Some occupied the benches, and two of them, both wearing hats, were rather shamefacedly eating soup, which struck Patrick as possibly an innovation by Mr O'Toole to reduce the late-night slaughter on the roads. With him, behind the bar, relentlessly serving, were two youths in white coats. The three or four men near the door nodded to Patrick, and one of them beamed at him, fixing him with a penetrating look.

This was a ragged, wild-looking individual, with three teeth and an enormously long nose, in a tattered coat that swung about him like a cloak.

'Ye are welcome,' he said, and bowed.

A Cork man.

The others were grinning.

'Thank you,' said Patrick.

'Cornelius O'Toole, lawful second cousin to the gintleman beyond, bids you welcome.'

'My name is Patrick Price-Jones. How do you do?'

'Oh there's a grand name for you!'

'Yours is pretty good too.'

The group laughed loudly. Cornelius, momentarily taken aback, quickly regained face.

'Oh, ho!' he said, 'I like your style. I like ye. And that's a fact.' He jabbed a bony finger towards Patrick.

'Will you have a drink?'

'Ah. Well now, I'll take a glass of stout with ye.'

Patrick thought it better not to patronise them all. He had a small Irish this time, because he had only just become aware that his growing sense of exhilaration was caused by the drinks being about four times the English measure. He noted the remarkable variety of bottles on the illuminated shelves behind Mr O'Toole, including every imaginable liqueur.

'You don't want to pay too much attention to my relative,' announced Mr O'Toole, serving him.

'You'll kindly look after your own affairs, and I'll look after mine,' said Cornelius with surprising asperity.

All smiles again, he inquired: 'And where are ye from?'

'Well . . . London.'

'My God, my goodness, is that right?'

'Yes.'

'And tell me now, would there be a nice job for me if I were to go across the water?'

'I don't really know. I don't think it's as easy as many people imagine.'

'Oh God, oh goodness. You don't say. Is that right?'

'People think the streets are going to be paved with gold . . .'

' 'Tis true, 'tis true.'

'And then they're disappointed.'

' 'Tis true, every word you're saying now. Oh, I like your style!'

Four men entered behind Patrick, and two of them were at once involved in badinage with Cornelius. Patrick found himself pressed into the centre of the room. Several men addressed him, but the noise was so great that it was difficult to hear. Mrs O'Sullivan revealed herself seated at the end of the bench, holding a pint of stout in her spacious lap. In her brother's emphatic voice she was saying to the man beside her: 'Ah, it's my poor dog, you know. He still has the old bronichal trouble.' Mostly Patrick seemed to be involved with two more smartly-dressed gentlemen, who were apparently successful operators in the cattle trade. The younger, who wore an American tie, was telling Patrick, to his surprise, that he had recently been staying with friends in Sunningdale and had gone up to the West End.

Patrick spoke of the traffic there.

The elder, a small, nervy man, hit the bar counter and shouted: 'We're sick to death over here of your West End and your East End!'

'I didn't know you ever heard about them,' declared Patrick in astonishment.

'We hear nothing else,' he said. 'I tell you we're sick to death of them.'

A new, unidentifiable sound was now apparent in the distance, and since the conversation was not particularly happy Patrick pushed through the crowd in that direction. A door appeared at the end of the bar with a large sign over it: 'No Singing.' From behind this door came the sound of a tenor voice raised loud in song. Patrick opened it and looked inside.

In another room, also small but painted green, a further twenty or so people were seated at tables, on kitchen chairs and along the benches, and they now included as many women as men. Most of them looked to be married women of a certain age, dressed up to a degree that made their husbands appear shabby, but there were a few younger ones, including two who were whispering in a corner. Everyone else wore an expression of reverence, the men with heads lowered, the women gazing frankly, with respect, at the singer. He was seated on a bench; an elderly, scrawny little farmer in a ragged overcoat, singing in a strained tenor with a crimson face, swelling veins, and a few brown teeth: 'Hold my hand. I'm a stranger in paradise.'

Patrick slipped into the vacant place on the bench by the door beside a woman with a large gin and tonic in her hand and a large white shiny bag on the table in front of her. The song ended. The singer cast his eyes on the floor, blushing and smiling with satisfaction, and a babel of applause and congratulations broke forth.

'You've surpassed yourself, Jimmy Keogh!' a man shouted.

"I'll hold your hand any time you say, Jimmy Keogh,' declared one of the women, and there were screams.

'Lovely!' said Patrick's neighbour. She leaned towards him in profile. 'Wasn't it lovely?'

'It was indeed,' he replied into her ear.

Everyone was now talking. The room was at the rear of the bar, and Mr O'Toole and his assistants had all this time been serving drinks through a small wooden hatch. In the uproar a pale, thin, grey-haired man in a double-breasted dark suit was mysteriously shouting: 'Next please! Next please!' He threw a fanatical glance at Patrick who quickly looked away. A moment later this individual was on his feet, moving from table to table with his right hand extended, as much as to say 'halt', and commanding, with passion: '*Ordher,* please! Ordher for the singer! Ordher, please!'

As a result a hush fell and it was revealed that for some time a crimson-faced farmer of about eighteen stone and of very rugged appearance had been on his feet and was well advanced in his song, 'My Mammy's Mammy'. His voice was hesitant and he appeared to be almost overcome. There were tears in his eyes. The woman who had been eager to hold Jimmy Keogh's hand began to assist, and the Master of Ceremonies whirled round upon her and whipped out: 'Ordher, please! Ordher for the singer!' She was silent. 'My mammy's mammy,' sang the giant, and he sat down, took out a large handkerchief and blew his nose, as applause and congratulations were again given without stint. 'Lovely!' said Patrick's neighbour. Above the tumult the M.C. demanded: 'Next, please! Next, please!'

'Ordher for the singer!' he was insisting a moment later. 'Ordher now, *please!*'

A dark-haired woman was singing, in a confident contralto, 'Some enchanted evening, you will see a stranger. You will hear his laughter . . .'

The two girls in the corner were still whispering. The M.C. was upon them.

'Listen here, you two. If you don't quit your gassin' you'll get a puck in the gob, d'yeh hear me?'

The girls looked mildly surprised, and were silent.

'. . . as long as you live, that laughter will haunt you . . .'

Patrick, studying the floor though now completely at ease, joined in softly almost without being aware of doing so.

'Ordher!'

He raised his eyes to see the M.C.'s pointing finger. 'Ordher there! One voice and one voice only, if you please!'

As he stopped the M.C. held him with a warning look.

'. . . ne-ver . . . let you . . . goooo,' sang the contralto, and she smiled, and after the applause was over Patrick heard himself say: 'Could we not have some Irish songs?'

'Ah, we're sick of all that ould stuff,' said Jimmy Keogh.

'You can say that again, Jimmy!'

There were murmurs of agreement from all over the room.

In the din, with the M.C. crying 'Next please!' Patrick called out: 'What about *you?*' The M.C. half turned, raised a warning hand and said, quietly this time: 'Ordher, please, ordher, please.' He devoted himself once more to the group across the room.

However, the affront had been noted, for suddenly he turned again and called out: 'This gentleman is next. Ordher, please!' and the noise, to Patrick's dismay, slowly diminished.

The room was silent.

The country of individuals was claiming him, in the person of this nightmarish M.C. If only they played darts, in communal silence, like the English.

'I can't, really. I don't honestly know the words of anything.'

'Ah, go on, give us a song,' said a kindly voice.

'Give us a verse or so, anyway.'

'Do what you can.'

'We're all friends here.'

'Well, the only song I know *is* an Irish song.'

'Ah sure it doesn't matther,' said Jimmy Keogh.

'It's no harm.'

'We don't mind, as long as you give us a song.'

'All right, then.'

He looked at the white handbag in front of him and began, in a faint but true voice, a difficult song which sobriety would have made unthinkable.

'My young love said to me, "My mother won't mind, and my father won't slight you . . ." '

'Ordher! Ordher, please!'

Cornelius O'Toole had appeared in the doorway immediately behind Patrick and was singing too, in a strong voice with many facial expressions.

'Ordher, please!'

Cornelius paid no attention, except to make another face. He and Patrick sang together. The M.C. was excited but nonplussed. Some men in the room behind Cornelius joined in too, whereupon several of the women in Patrick's room followed suit.

In moving chorus they sang of how the ghost of 'my young love' came 'as I lay sleeping'. The M.C. sat down '. . . and this she did say, "It will not be long, love, till our wedding day." '

No one spoke for a moment.

Then Jimmy Keogh said: 'Well done, well done, indeed. You've a *voice,* sir.'

'About twenty voices,' said Patrick, laughing.

'No, no.'

'You did very well.'

'Very well, altogether.'

The other room was now singing in chorus. At once the women in Patrick's room began something quite different: 'I could have danced all night . . .' The M.C. was silent. The entire public house was now giving voice. Patrick's neighbour had unexpectedly linked arms with him and they were both engaged upon 'I could have spread my wings, and done a thousand things . . .' He was overtaken by a wholly delightful sense of community which presented this outwardly unlovely place and its occupants as the perfect ending to a journey of discovery that had only begun that morning. He could have sung all night. But one of the white-coated youths was now in the doorway, announcing with conscious dramatic effect: 'Squad car!'

Instantly the room was silent, as were the other rooms. His neighbour detached her arm and joined a procession with three other women and a dozen men, including the M.C., which without a word having been uttered and with no appearance of haste moved out through a door decorated with the large notice, in black on white: GENTS.

An instant later Cornelius O'Toole came in through the same door, wearing an expression of incredulity and shock.

'What about us?' said Patrick, apprehensively. 'It must be rather crowded in there.'

'It's O.K.,' said Mr O'Toole, entering. 'False alarm. That lad's new. The poor boy isn't able to distinguish between a squad car and a radio cab.'

An ear must have been placed to the door because the four women at once came out of the Gents, followed by the twelve men. Smiling a little, they took their places again and, the formality over, recommenced singing.

But, whether or not because of the false alarm, it was not long before Mr O'Toole was declaring, in the voice of Jehovah: 'Time now, ladies and gentlemen, *please.*'

Patrick rose and returned to the other room where he found that he was compelled to lean on the counter for support. One of the assistants was helping three of the customers to raise a fourth who had fallen backwards and lay rigid upon the floor. Mr O'Toole came to Patrick's end of the counter, indicated his glass, and thundered: 'Let's have your glasses now, *please,*' at once adding, *sotto voce:* 'Not you.' He moved away, shouting. Reluctantly the company thinned. Wondering whether or not to finish, Patrick met the gaze of a dark, unshaven, wild-eyed man lingering near the door who clearly had no intention of submitting to any distinctions. Mr O'Toole returned, roared: 'Your glasses, *please,* gentlemen,' and added in the same murmur: 'Not you.' But when the number was reduced to five, including the madman, Patrick moved to the door. 'I'd better go home,' he said, as Mr O'Toole came from behind the counter. They went out through the porch into the chill moonlit night. The company was vanishing into the darkness, singing. Patrick was standing out on the sloping road and Mr O'Toole in the open glass doorway of the porch. 'You seem happy to be back,' he said, his breath visible in the night air.

'I am indeed,' replied Patrick. 'This is the finest country in the world, and you, Mr O'Toole, run the finest pub.'

Mr O'Toole placed a hand up against the glass side of the porch, and leaning against it looked at him for what seemed a long time.

'Ah, yes,' he said, 'yes. You come to see the peepshow.'

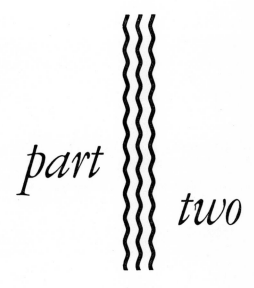

part *two*

chapter eleven

Now it was beginning, thought Grania, seated in the back of the Bentley. Now anything might happen, and this, even more than her home, was what she came here for. She sat between Hilda and Patrick under a fur rug, looking slim in a suit of scarlet baneen, purchased in Ireland and assembled in Paris. The presence of Flanagan at the wheel forbade discussion of the subject which had oppressed them for a week; though indeed it was not to be discussed in her father's presence either. He merely awaited a remedy, and as yet they were speechless. They had lunched early and were now on the way to Dermot's show. The fur rug was superfluous because the afternoon was astonishingly mild and sunny. It was November and ought by now to have been like living at the bottom of a tank. Hilda wore her mink cape, but had changed symbolically from black to emerald underneath.

The sense of well-being and suppressed excitement was so great that the vision of the back of Flanagan's head, in his chauffeur's hat, conjured up a pleasantly wistful rather than sad memory of André's remark: 'Your Celtic treasure drives well.'

He was talking.

'Oh, a desperate dream, madam. One of those great Rubens ladies, from the flat in London, came out of the frame at me, flying down from the clouds in her shift, waving her great big sword. It was perfectly fantastic. It put the heart across me, I can tell you.'

'I can imagine, Flanagan,' she said.

'How very quaint,' remarked Hilda.

'It was more than quaint, madam. I woke up all of a tremble. I think I screamed. I declare to God I was bathed in perspiration, if you'll pardon the expression. But truly.'

'Dear me,' said Grania. Was it really a fact, she wondered, that she liked him only for his subservience; and had it perhaps been the same with her husbands? André was very different: sometimes frightening.

The sun shone kindly on the old crumbling stone walls that towered above the road and the occasional pavements. Against them, at intervals, at the country bus stops, stood small clusters of people waiting to catch the bus into town. They were poor, shabby, ignorant and remote. Her Ireland did not embrace them, nor the ragged children who played with a dirty tennis-ball in the road until Flanagan hooted with a finger of his white driving-glove and they scattered and the Bentley drifted silently past. Her affinity with Dermot must be in part an Irishness that they shared. It was a little disturbing to be reminded that it was so exclusive. The Neelan houses were on the right now. They were hideous, certainly, but had recently been fresh, bright and new. It was remarkable how quickly they had been reduced to a squalor of apparent long-standing; with their grey muslin curtains, broken window-panes, and the familiar Irish phenomenon of rusted tin-cans and rotting bicycle tyres decorating the garden plot among the more explicable paper litter. More than half of them had undergarments hanging out to dry in the sunshine. Farther on the new Catholic church presented itself. It was equally alien.

'Do you think we may expect any scenes today?' asked Patrick.

'I doubt it, darling,' she replied. 'I rather think they're reserved for the British public.'

'Oh, what a pity,' said Hilda.

'I was there, you know, at the Venetian exhibition in St James's,' Grania remarked, 'when he declared that it was sewage from the canals and fell down and was carried out by two attendants and the chairman of the organising committee.'

Flanagan uttered a shrill laugh.

Patrick had always found him extremely irritating.

'You know a lot about painting,' he said to his mother, 'I don't.

But apart from that, he does seem to be the wrong Irish representative abroad. Isn't it about time we were known for the quality and dignity that Grandfather talks about?'

'I thought he said there wasn't any here, dear,' said Hilda.

'The rare individual is quite enough for me,' said Grania.

'I agree,' said Hilda.

'I think it wonderful that a country should be known for one of its artists.'

'Oh, really, Mother! For drinking and boorishness, you mean.'

'No, no. Artists have unusual habits. Even the English know that.'

'Doesn't "civilised" mean anything? Like it used to do.'

'It ought never to mean being well-behaved and a bore. It means being a real, complete person, with compassion; which is certainly Dermot.'

'It only seems like that because he hasn't done the expected and knocked you down. Compassion is less obvious in quiet people.'

'Don't be silly, dear.'

The low winter sun made the tall Georgian curve of Harcourt Street glow redly, and emphasised the proportions of the windows. Stephen's Green behind its railings was no less attractive.

'I believe Henry is doing a bust of Yeats for the Green,' said Grania. 'I hope it's a start at last. Even London has Irving and Shakespeare. Our great lack is respect. We want to go one better now and name the streets after artists. I've always thought we could make a Paris here. We have the river, and its old antique shops and charming bridges. We have an atmosphere. Half the city is writing novels, in speech at last. And yet I suppose that's why none of them read, and why there's no respect. Why should they be silent, after all? The writer draws on them. Their speech is his life-blood.'

'According to Grandfather, that can only be true now in outposts of the West.'

'He's always been so desperately gloomy.'

She had received a letter that morning from her sister, Delia, which she had been obliged to conceal from her father. In almost illegible handwriting it detailed a new extravagance. Delia was in possession of some ruined mansion in Paris where she was living with the poet, Arcoli, and watching over him while he died of cirrhosis of the liver. Meanwhile she played host daily to the artists and writers, Marc Albert Louvessin, Jean Marat, Henri Duplessis, François Gramont, Paulette Nin, Otto Kranz and Monika, and at their persuasion was planning to finance a new magazine to be entitled *A,* meaning the origin and basic essence of all things. Her connection with artists had always been less objective than Grania's.

Flanagan drove off Dawson Street under the archway into the garage of the Royal Irish Automobile Club. He was to be left to his own devices for an hour, while they walked to the gallery. This place had changed, Grania had noted before. A new type had infiltrated. As they were going out she heard two such women following behind them.

'Well, I need hardly tell you, Maureen, when Jim turned up on the Fridah I got the shock o' me life!'

'You don't say! God, I can imagine!'

'As usual, of course, he was two parts gone. That's nothin' new. Anyway . . .'

The trio walked down Dawson Street in the sunshine, with the uplifting vista, at the bottom, of the grey heights of Trinity rising above the bare trees. Featured aloft, in front of the charming residence of the Lord Mayor of Dublin, a new red Austin Seven advertised itself as being up for public lottery. Patrick had a feeling that everyone in the village would take a ticket. He was re-experiencing the sensation of his arrival, of homeliness and sanity, of a place just the right size; friends available in their long-adopted bars, and the sea and the mountains twenty minutes away. There must be a means of staying. In what fair sense had Mr. O'Toole considered him alien? Down here was not O'Sullivan's bar: it was a village, maybe, but also a capital.

One large Sleator was exhibited in the window of the gallery.

On a vibrant purple plain, established with thick paint, ancient Irish crosses, or rather the abstract semblance of them, stood subsiding to left and right like so many grey symbols of past glory and present decay. The impression, however, was not in the least sad. The painting might have been, and probably was, executed in a state of intoxication. Grania knew that no symbolism was intended.

'You see,' she said. 'A great talent.'

'It's quite fantastic,' said Hilda.

Beyond the painting, through the window, the small gallery contained about thirty people, holding sherry glasses in their hands and making a considerable noise.

They went through the glass doorway.

Lawrence Hurley, the owner of the gallery, took Grania's hand. He was the son of a tailor in Tralee, but looked nothing like it, except that his suit was well cut. He was tall and slim and wore a gold chain over his double-breasted waistcoat. He was known to Sleator as 'the pimp'; which was unkind, since he was a man of sensibility and courage. He had twice been called upon by representatives of the Faith in view of the exhibition of naked bodies, once in sculpture, once in oils. He had ushered the priests out firmly, and on the second occasion not too politely, and refused to place the offending works out of sight. Like Delia, he would have preferred to be in Paris, but he derived satisfaction from fostering the arts of his own country, and, more particularly, he was in a profitable position to advise the new bourgeoisie on their purchases and to effect them without much difficulty.

He received Hilda with great courtesy. He had recently been to London to 'refresh his flagging spirits', which she found 'naughty of you. I'm sure you don't mean it. I'm over here for the same purpose.'

Grania led them forward into the throng. On seeing her, the artist himself broke the circle which surrounded him. Dermot Sleator at first sight appeared to be a huge pair of horn-rimmed spectacles and an enormous bald-domed head. Small eyes were then to be observed behind the glasses, and a blunt upturned nose, unshaven black stubble on his jowls, and black hair in his ears. He wore a huge sweater that was once white, from which plump hands protruded, appearing to be ingrained with the purple paint seen in the picture in the window. He had rubbed some of it on to his bald head with an habitual nervous gesture.

'Grania, me Protestant queen,' he said, taking her slender hand in his fat one and kissing it. 'Me dark Rosaleen.' He was sweating. 'Who's that wid yeh?'

'Hilda Manningham, an old friend of mine.'

'How are yeh, Hilda, me ould duck.'

'How do you do?'

'That's a nice bit o' cat you're wearin'. And is this the fruit o' your loins?'

'It's Patrick,' said Grania. 'I don't think we need elaborate.'

'They've taught him cricket. I'm glad to see that. You can always tell. Bejasus I wish I was your age again and knew what I know now. What ails yeh?' he roared at Hurley's young woman assistant, who was attempting to murmur in his ear.

'Listen to me, my sweet virgin. Tell the lady this isn't a bargain basement. Let her go to O'Connell Street.'

'Your pictures are quite delightful,' said Hilda, looking round the flaming walls.

'They're not delightful,' said the artist, 'they're bloody well brilliant. Full of bloody depth. I'll be back.'

He had moved towards a new arrival. He seemed extremely restless.

They were offered, and accepted, glasses of sherry. 'What a charmer,' said Hilda to Patrick's surprise. He found himself facing the smiling 'Teeth' Murphy, the dentist on the Arts Council, a big friendly man with a ginger moustache. In a moment Patrick was telling him about leaving his London job. 'Teeth' had this professional gift for extractions. As a result he was filled with information, which he would, in turn, give in such a pleasant and exceptionally uninteresting way that afterwards it was impossible to remember a word that he had said. He was charming to Hilda. She was beginning to encounter a genuine curiosity about herself that was most disarming.

Patrick escaped and looked about him. It was difficult to see the pictures. He noted Dermot's friend, Martin O'Keeffe, the writer, talking to his mother. It was he who had removed her painting by AE of the fairy in the bog, not presumably for love but for money. She was bringing them both to *The Kiss of Death* that night. He was a thin, intense young man in a blue fisherman's jersey, with a sharp nose and a way of nodding it up and down like a bird as he talked. Near-by, Dan Lavelle, an elegant young man and Ireland's first male couturier, was talking to a plump woman decorated with pearls, in a black dress probably made by him. There was also 'Twitcher' Doyle, a district justice renowned for witticisms in the rural courts and for a tic in both cheeks; and Terence Keogh, the Royal Hibernian Academician.

Since he was a member of a camp permanently at war with Sleator and the 'modern' group, it was an act of generosity for him to be here. Moreover he was actually going round the pictures. He was doing so with two extremely stout Franciscans, in brown habits and sandals, from whom he was seldom separated. The trio looked odd since the monks were short and Keogh was very tall and thin, with a splendid mop of grey hair. He was a man of real culture who, from time to time, went into long periods of study and retirement in Trinity College Library. He was the kind of companion Patrick's grandfather seemed to require, but with the only too apparent obstacle of the Franciscans. He had once painted magnificently but under the pressure of a closed society and the need for support had degenerated into fashionable portraiture. From this he sought solace in drink, and further relief in the Church.

A woman had joined these three and was talking animatedly to the monks. Patrick recognized Mrs Neelan. She was wearing the same beige suit and hat with a veil in which she had met her husband at the airport, and a beige coat with a fur collar. She had noticed him, and to his surprise broke off her conversation and moved closer.

In the agreeable Dublin way that omitted all preliminaries, Moira leaned towards him and whispered:

'Wait till my husband hears the Franciscans were here. He'll have a fit! He thinks Sleator is anti-Christ.'

It struck him that this was not solely Dublin informality, but was also connected with the empty sherry-glass in her hand.

'Have you met my daughter, by the way?'

'No, I haven't.'

A taller, dark-haired and attractive girl was standing behind her.

'Ann, come over. This is Mr Patrick Price-Jones, a neighbour of ours.'

'Hallo.' She smiled in an amusing way.

'She has a bee in her bonnet about London. I hope you'll tell her different. Is your mother here, by the way?'

'Yes, she's there in the corner.'

'Would you ever take me over to her? Woops, what on earth did they put in that sherry? I was nearly tripping over meself.'

She had seized his elbow in a manner reminiscent of her husband.

He interrupted his mother, who was still involved with Martin O'Keeffe. There were handshakes and introductions that included the daughter, Ann. O'Keeffe looked displeased. Grania presented her most gracious and false smile.

'My husband says I was lacking in what he calls *politesse* at the airport, though I assure you it was never meant,' said Moira. 'I've come over to make amends.'

'How sweet of you,' said Grania. 'My son said the same thing of me, in rather stronger terms.'

'Did he now?'

Moira looked at Patrick with new and friendly interest.

'Men are sensitive creatures, are they not?'

'They are indeed,' Grania agreed.

'Pah!' said O'Keeffe, but no one noticed.

'As a matter of fact,' said Moira, 'I've been meaning to call at Edenmore for a long time now. I can't imagine why I've never got round to it. Of course you're not often there, are you?'

'From time to time,' replied Grania.

'I heard you were at Cannes—with a friend,' said Moira. 'Norah Gerraty saw you.'

'Who?'

'Norah Gerraty, the wife of . . . the architect.'

'Oh, I know. The handsome one.'

'Well . . . I suppose so.'

'I shouldn't have thought it was in doubt, if I remember rightly. And are you enjoying . . . Hill View, isn't it?'

'It is. Well, to tell you the truth it's a bit lonely up there. It's cut off, don't you know. I mean, it's hard to keep servants for instance.'

'Oh, but of course. My Finola Doyle used to be with you.'

'She was. That's right.'

'I think she prefers to be closer to town, or something.'

'Maybe so. I have her sister, Kathleen, you know. This morning she didn't bring me my tea and I found her shut in her bedroom in a state. My God, they'd wear you out.'

'They would indeed. Finola, on the contrary, has been forgetting everything for the past week through high spirits. Singing about the house. But we mustn't talk about the servants, you know, Mrs Neelan. Men don't like it. My father *strongly* disapproves.'

'Norah Gerraty says he's sweet.'

'I beg your pardon?'

'Your father. Norah says he's sweet.'

'Your friend appears to have a vivid imagination.'

'She's more tanned than you are, if you don't mind my saying so.'

'Not at all. I hear, by the way, that your husband has hopes of starting another of his delightful building schemes.'

'He has hopes of more than that, though I shouldn't be saying it!'

'Really? How interesting. I trust that nothing will stand in his way. I do admire your hat, incidentally. It's most becoming. I'm afraid I never wear one. Sheer laziness.'

Patrick turned to Ann Neelan, who was standing beside him.

'This doesn't seem to be going too well,' he murmured, moving away. 'I find it embarrassing.'

'So do I.'

'Let's look at the pictures. After all, it's what we're supposed to be here for.'

They stood in front of a vast brown and black semi-abstraction representing bogland.

'You've gone pale,' she said. 'Men *must* be sensitive.'

'I find it distressing when decent people won't show a little tolerance towards each other.'

'Mother is naturally frank. She doesn't understand that others can see harm in it?'

'I think she intended a little harm, don't you?'

'Maybe a little,' said Ann, smiling.

'It's nearly always women. The feminine ego is a terrible thing.'

'Is that what your grandfather says?'

'I hadn't thought of it, but I suppose it is, yes. How did you guess?'

'It sounded like it from what your mother was saying.'

Moira interrupted them, rather coolly:

'Darling, I'm having tea with Terence and the Franciscans. Can you amuse yourself?'

'Of course.'

'I'll see you at the theatre. Your mother's leaving,' she added to Patrick, and moved away.

'Why don't we have tea somewhere?' he suggested.

'I'd love to. Would you like to see how a Dubliner lives? I'll show you my dingy lodgings. I've a gas-ring.'

'Fine. I'll just tell her.'

His mother had linked arms with Martin O'Keeffe and Dermot in the doorway.

'We are in need of stronger refreshment,' she said. 'Are you coming?'

'I think I'll stay a while. I haven't really looked at the pictures.'

'Holy God,' said Dermot.

'Are you feeling all right, dear?'

'Yes, perfectly.'

'Are you sure you won't come to the play?'

'Quite sure. I'll go home with Grandfather. I'll ring him at the shop, as arranged.'

'Very well. Oh dear, where's Hilda gone to? Hilda!'

Hilda was talking with animation to Dan Lavelle. She broke it off with exaggerated farewells.

'I've had such fun,' she said.

'We'll bring it to a climax,' said Dermot. 'Come on owa that. I'm thirsty.'

They went out into Wicklow Street, and the four of them linked together, they swept the pavement clear.

'Twenty minutes to the Holy Hour,' said Dermot. 'We haven't much time, girls.'

They walked up Grafton Street, which was alive with pedestrians, and entered Davy Byrne's.

'I've got to cash a cheque at the Bank of Ireland,' said Dermot, seating himself in a corner. 'The pimp has been gracious enough to cough up, and I've promised to assist Terence Keogh, the poor bastard.'

'We'll drive down,' said Grania. 'We're meeting Flanagan at the club at half-past.'

'The whore he inadvertently wedded is calling for support from Mullingar, through some local shysters. I wish he'd got her that time in the marquee, d'you remember?'

'I do indeed. He nearly got me.'

'Who owned the station-wagon? I've wondered.'

'Lord Tedesale.'

'He has a bloody fine weapon there, if her ladyship proves tiresome.'

Drinks were ordered, and Dermot consumed two large whiskies, neat, in a few moments.

'Well,' he said, drawing the back of his hand across the lower part of his face, 'who was privileged to cast an uncomprehending eye upon my works? And what have you to say in your defence? One at a time.'

'I saw them,' said Martin, gazing palely at the table, 'and I considered them a betrayal.'

'Oh, ho! And will the lad be brazen enough to say who—or what—they bloody well betrayed?'

'Ireland. Your country.' Martin looked him in the eye and dipped his nose like a bird. 'We've had enough of your commercial lies, Dermot Sleator, and your beautiful bogs. You are surrounded by tragedy and you shut your eyes and sing.'

'Martin, what on earth are you talking about?' demanded Grania.

Martin ran a finger round inside the collar of his blue jersey and nervously drank his whisky.

'I respect you,' he said, with intensity. 'Since you've become a success, there's all of a sudden about three people left in the country who'll tolerate you, and I'm one of them. Except for the working class, to whom you're a celebrity—and a joke. I admire anyone who can rise from this mire of mediocre mutual esteem. But it's all the more reason why you should show a sense of responsibility.'

'Christ preserve us! Were you at Eton?'

'Why don't you paint the reality—the tragedy?'

Martin had picked up a beer-mat and was pointing it at Dermot.

'Put that thing down. It's apt to go off. I suppose it's our damned revolution again. The heroes betrayed. I couldn't care bloody well less. I wasn't concerned. I was an infant, a respect-

able member of the middle classes, a son of a bank manager in
Limerick . . .'

'You don't have to tell me.'

'And you weren't even born.'

'I was born among the working class and soon enough to know
the real hero of what you call a revolution. James Connolly
fought for a socialist workers' republic . . .'

'Oh, Holy God.'

'Not merely freedom, but freedom from want and exploitation.
What happened?'

'Don't hesitate to tell us.'

'In the forty years the gifted Irish have been turned into a na-
tion of blasted puppets. They were never so exploited! As for
want, look at the children of the poor. You don't have to go far.
Our thought-machine is the equal of Russia's. We have our forbidden authors too. Nothing flourishes, only the gombeen-man.'

'The who?' asked Hilda.

'Irish for usurer, me ould duck,' said Dermot, rubbing more
purple on to his head in a tired way. The exhibition had reduced
him.

'A gombeen's paradise they've made. Building their motels,
making their films. Local players getting their five pounds a day
as Black and Tans—four pounds more than the Tans got. "God,
if me poor father could see me now." Ah, it makes you sick!
Films, but no Abbey built as yet, of course. Not that it's any
harm. The kitchen comedy has been replaced by the suburban
comedy. Vile rubbish for the new middle class.'

'That's not fair,' said Dermot. 'They're doing *Private Lives* at
the Gate.'

'Yes, we've a new class-tiered society now. No welfare state for
us. Too Christian a notion for our spiritual leaders.'

'No classes in England, I suppose? You poor ould peasant!'

'No hunger, no rickets, at any rate. The gombeen-men have
been here, you see. Out with the sawdust and in with the chromium."

'I think it's a great improvement,' said Grania. She was enjoying herself immensely. The afternoon was turning out exactly as she had hoped.

'And in the process they've removed the wall of the Gents that was covered with the autographs of everyone who mattered when Dublin had a great cultural life.'

'You poor bloody sentimentalist! Another Gents gone.'

'It seems to me,' said Hilda bravely, 'that the country is improving itself in every way. It's coming in line with Europe. What's wrong with cleanliness and being modern? You've ceased to be an island and are looking outwards.' She lowered her high-pitched voice. 'I've noticed that two men at the bar are reading the *Daily Express* and another one is reading the *Daily Mail.*'

'My dear woman,' said Martin, 'they are reading William Hickey and Tanfield's Diary, where matters are printed that are not permitted by the national thought-machine in our own organs. They frequently include the wilder doings of Dermot Sleator.'

'I'm pleased to say I agree with you, for once,' said Dermot.

'It stinks, the whole set-up. It's really tragic. I tell you, we could have become a society which would have been to the world the apotheosis of Christianity.'

'O Holy Mary, guard and protect us. Not that one, please not that one.'

'Instead we live in a socially decadent, economically bankrupt and intellectually arid gombeen's paradise. And you, Dermot Sleator, rejoice in the ancient crosses and the bloody bogs!'

'But surely,' said Hilda, 'painting has nothing to do with politics?'

'You've put your ould finger on it this time, Hilda me dear,' said Dermot.

'Everything has to do with politics. Whether he likes it or not this man stands, or staggers would be more like, for this country.'

'Oh, you nasty insulting thing! Talking of crosses, I walked upright into Ireland's own museum this morning to look at them again, and by God they're bloody marvellous, though it's a pity they've been covered with chocolate. I did *not* visit the death-masks and the automatic with the long snout surrendered by poor dear Countess Markievitch. It's not even pitiful. And there was this fellah up the ladder giving the great cross of Monaster-boice, A.D. 700, the once over with the vacuum-cleaner, and sing-ing 'Love Is a Many-Splendoured Thing'. Electric wires all over the floor, like snakes. Lovely echo for singing. It has a vault, you know. The sun coming through and love resounding from every crevice. Altogether delightful. I suppose you would have wept?'

'Ah shut up.'

Martin was becoming pale and silent and intoxicated, and Der-mot flushed and loud and intoxicated.

'This young orator writes short stories, you know, Hilda my dear, and I declare now to God that the world revealed there is outside my ken. I sometimes have a nasty thought that it is a literary fabrication dating from many years ago and perpetuated by machinery. Master O'Keeffe's characters have four ages. First, the chisler with the rickets beside the railings in Gardiner Street. Then the student—mortal sin and the sodalities and the hairy priest whacking away with the ruler. Then the youth—a most miserable seduction by the hotel maid in a bunker, at Portmar-nock, in the rain. Then the civil servant, creeping out at six in the rain for a drink with an equally ageing butty and a dirty memory of days gone by, after a day filled with ink-stains and the odour of ancient blotting-paper. God hand me the eau-de-Cologne. Where is this life? Where are these people?'

'They're not in London at any rate. My God, I'd like to be there.'

'Ah, London, London. Moscow, Moscow. Why don't you get up and go?'

'Time, please! Your glasses now, ladies and gentlemen, *please.*'

'Very well, then,' said Dermot. 'We shall now drink a toast to the Interviewer.'

'To the who?' asked Grania.

'The Interviewer. London Transport requires men and women aged twenty or more. The Interviewer will be at Moran's Hotel, Talbot Street, all day Wednesday, Thursday, Friday. Candidates A to H on the first, I to S on the second, T to Y, the third. Fares paid to London of accepted applicants. Note, however, if you please. Positions outside Ireland. Before accepting positions of employment outside this country, readers are advised to satisfy themselves as to facilities offered to practise their religion. The Catholic Social Welfare Bureau, God love them, will inquire for you. I give you now—the Interviewer!'

'The Interviewer,' said Grania.

'The Interviewer,' said Hilda.

'The Interviewer,' murmured Martin.

They drank.

'And let's hope the candidate hasn't consumption,' said Martin.

The sun was still shining when they went out. They looked colourful and different beside the drabness of most of the other people crowding the streets; Grania, Dermot and Martin in red, white and blue, and Hilda in emerald green. Several people stopped, recognising Dermot from the British newspapers. Once seen in a photograph, the large bald head was not easily missed. Aware of the colour scheme, with his painter's eye, he said: 'Hilda walks in green, in external association with the Commonwealth.'

'I must say,' she remarked, having no idea what he was talking about, 'I was received with extraordinary kindness at the exhibition. People met me as if I was a celebrity or something, and as if anything I had to say must be of the greatest possible interest.'

'They're hungry, the poor bloody wretches,' said Dermot.

'It's more than that,' said Grania. 'It's the native interest in all people.'

'Not a bit of it,' Dermot insisted. 'Ever since we threw the stranger out we've been starving to meet one. We're sick of each other. That English mummer, Lorrimer, that we're going to see tonight, has already given about six interviews to the local press.'

'I bet you're jealous,' said Martin.

'What I don't understand about you, Martin,' said Grania, 'is why with all that James Connolly business you tolerate me?'

'We're just a couple of snobs,' said Dermot.

'People of position who know how to live are all right. I admire them. It's the jumped-up middle classes I can't abide.'

'Les extrèmes se touchent,' pronounced Dermot, very badly. 'It's a philosophy that's gained many a poor bloody man a weekend in a wealthy home, and other patronage besides.'

'Rubbish,' said Martin. 'I'm one of the people who should have been born rich. I genuinely enjoy caviare.'

'Oh, ho!' roared Dermot.

At the corner of Dawson Street a woman in a shawl approached, whining: 'Violets. Lovely violets.'

'No thank you,' said Grania.

She closed in on Dermot, demanding, in a lower voice: 'Would you ever spare a penny for a cup o' tea, misther?'

He handed her a florin from his trouser pocket, saying: 'Tea's gone up since you were a girl, my dear.'

'The blessings of God and His Holy Mother go with you. I'll say a prayer for you tonight.'

'You're a decent bloody woman.'

'The professional compassionate,' said Martin as they walked on.

'Oh cheer up or dry up!'

'You *are* gloomy today, Martin,' said Grania. 'I feel I should point out to Hilda that you're not always like this.'

'It happens here. You can't breathe.'

'As long as you can still drink,' said Dermot, 'it doesn't much matter.'

'I don't share these feelings,' said Grania.

'Stay a while longer this time,' Martin advised.

'I'm staying till Christmas at least.'

'We'll have a bloody party,' Dermot suggested.

'What a good idea!'

'Oh do let's,' said Hilda.

'We must discuss it, though perhaps not with Father. I'm still thinking about the gombeen-men. I'm sorry to go on about it, but I agree with Hilda. I've enough faith in the Irish to believe that they would survive cleanliness and modernity. If your gombeen-men would put some attractive restaurants and hotels into the pits of squalor that are called Irish country towns and villages, it would reduce emigration by thousands. At present the country supplies half the waitresses in London. Everyone knows they'd far rather stay home if there was work. It's only the sophisticates like Martin who dream of the bright lights, or the restless ones who would travel anyhow. Why can't a respectable woman—admittedly with different tastes to my own—be served with a single cup of tea between here and Galway?'

'Yes,' said Martin. 'Let's make it a land fit for tourists.'

'She can always have a drink with five toothless near-mental deficients in a bar so dark that it will take her five minutes to adjust her eyesight to the rather alarming company. But a restaurant free from ptomaine poisoning, no. It's like crossing the steppes. Why?'

'Let grasses grow and waters flow.
In a free and easy way.
But give me enough of the rare old stuff
That's made near Galway Bay.'

Dermot was singing, in a rumbling bass. It was a familiar occurrence to Grania and Martin. Only Hilda gave it much attention.

'The gaugers all from Donegal,
Sligo and Leitrim too,

Oh, we'll give them the slip and we'll take a sip
Of the real old Mountain Dew.'

'It's the only gain left us by press, pulpit and politicians,' said
Martin. 'The countryside survives them, and the gombeen-men
too. In England you have tea and scones all the way, and no
countryside.'

'It's no gain at all,' said Hilda. 'Why not make it a land fit for
its own people?'

'A land of waitresses?'

'You don't understand our young revolutionary,' said Dermot.
'His idea is to end want without providing work. That's what he
means by a welfare state.'

They had gone in under the archway. The Bentley was there,
but no Flanagan. The two women and Martin sat in the back,
and Dermot in the front, singing again:

'About four years ago I was digging the land
With my brogues on my feet and my spade in my hand,
Says I to myself: "What a pity to see
Such a fine strapping lad footing turf in Tralee".'

It was rather dark and cold in the garage.

'Let's have more gombeen-men, I say,' continued Grania. 'The
man this country needs is Joe Lyons. He's given a million Irish
girls a decent life. Why not have clean, well-run restaurants so
that the wretched Irish women may come out from behind their
yashmaks and eat and drink in public, and let their daughters
serve them, for once.'

'I feel sure your father would say it was the last straw,' Hilda
remarked.

'Another England. Demi-paradise,' said Martin. 'We've no tradition of eating out. It requires centuries of decay.'

'So mother heaves water and turns the spit,' said Grania. 'Wait till she has television and sees the advertisements, and a damn good thing too!'

'Ruin.'

'Oh, who will plough the field now, or who will sell the corn?
Oh, who will wash the sheep now and have them nicely shorn?'

'What ruin? Do you really think it will change the Irish? Do you think it will alter Dermot? Are our people so vulnerable? Nonsense. We toasted the Interviewer. We should have toasted his admirable opponent, the Gombeen-man.'

Flanagan emerged from the club and came hurrying to the window.

'Gracious, madam, I didn't know you were here. I was inside, having a chat with Lady Hankworth.'

'Really?'

'She used to be a friend of the Terenures when I was with them,' explained Flanagan, moving in to the driving-seat beside Dermot. 'At least, when I say a friend, she has no more opinion of them than I do myself, to speak quite truthfully.'

'I'm glad I rescued you, Flanagan. Tell me, would you have stayed in Cahirciveen if a suitable employment had presented itself?'

'My gracious! It's a dear little place, madam, but I'm afraid it's not quite me.'

'One can see that,' said Dermot, 'though you'd look well in a kilt, piping while the ladies took tea.'

'Oh dear, I think you must be having me on, as they say.'

Flanagan had driven out of the garage and they were going down Dawson Street again.

'I suppose it's frightfully English of me,' said Hilda, 'but I still don't understand what all that was about in the pub. What has economics got to do with painting?'

'It's a question of *feeling* about economics,' said Martin, 'or about anything. The man is shallow, in human terms. Is that better? He has no sense of tragedy. He feels nothing underneath.'

'Oh, my God, man, we all do,' shouted Dermot, with sudden passion. They could see the back of his neck turning red. 'We know all about that. It's not worth expressing. My bloody eyes were given me to show the joys. For God's sake, grow up!'

'There are other emotions that are both more profound and more universal, that's all.'

'I must say I come here to escape emotions,' said Grania, 'because they *are* so universal and boring and damn destructive. I'll admit it's the one great advantage of a man's country that they're at a minimum here, where womanly passions provoked only disinterest and alarm, and in consequence are short-lived.'

'O woman shapely as a swan,

On your account I shall not die!' said Dermot. 'Padraic Colum, from the mediæval Gaelic.'

'Exactly. And the sense of peace, the absence of time, the soft air, and particularly the pungent native sense of humour, are all against emotions. So is Martin's friend, the Church. Novels are spoken or written here; seldom performed. We only play games, but like the juggler in the Anatole France story we play them to the greater glory of God. Dermot is a master hand.'

'My dear,' said Hilda, 'I never dreamed you could be so philosophical.'

'I'm at my worst with Father. He unnerves me. I never dreamed that you could be either, Hilda, to tell the truth. I've been impressed.'

'Ireland reveals us all in the end,' remarked Dermot.

'Our unique selves,' said Grania, 'not our shared emotions. I think I'm a little drunk—which also helps.'

'So it's to be juggling instead of passion?' said Martin.

'The Metropole's showing *The Lady's in Love,*' said Dermot. 'We'll drop you off there.'

'I don't think I've ever met a single juggler in England,' said Grania.

'God help them,' said Dermot. 'Blame the Romans.'

'In that case the Romans have greatly improved. There's a second Irish gift, of course: destructiveness. That's where Martin comes in.'

'Hilda, your cheek-bones are bloody marvellous,' said Dermot. 'At least they are in the mirror. I'm going to paint you.'

'How heavenly! Do you mean it?'

'Of course I bloody well mean it. We'll go there now. I'll start at once.'

'He has a very grand studio in Fitzwilliam Square,' Grania explained.

'How exciting.'

'Since we're becoming intimate, where's what the poor English call "hubby"? I noted the ring.'

'That has to do with emotions,' said Grania. 'Let's leave it.'

'Thank you, dear,' said Hilda.

'I must say, you've never painted *me*.'

'There's no paint black enough for your dusky locks, my dark Rosaleen.'

'O my dark Rosaleen,
Do not sigh, do not weep!
The priests are on the ocean green,
They march along the deep.
There's wine from the royal Pope
Upon the ocean green;
And Spanish ale shall give you hope,
My dark Rosaleen!'

'I like a song,' said Flanagan.

'I haven't bloody well finished it yet.'

'I think you'd better, dear,' said Grania. 'The bank will be closing in a minute.'

They had drawn up and were seated in the forecourt. To the left the semi-circular sweep of railings separated them from College Green. To the right the immense pillars towered above them, supporting the pediment that bore the royal coat of arms of the former House of Lords, which had survived so many anonymous phone-calls over the years. Dermot left them, mounted the stone steps, passed between the great pillars, and so inside.

'What fun we've had,' said Hilda. 'I never thought I'd spend a whole afternoon just talking. Does anybody else besides your father go to work here?'

'I believe a few do,' replied Grania, 'but not very seriously.'

'I'm afraid I'm being awfully England again,' said Hilda, 'but I haven't gathered whether you gentlemen are Protestant or Catholic.'

'Ah, you're asking the right questions at last,' said Martin. 'As you might have guessed, our friend was born to the juggler's creed of Shaw and Wilde—non-practising; and I to the One True Faith—lapsed.'

'I see.'

'You'd better be careful, my dear,' said Grania. 'You seem to have made a hit with him. I've never heard him say "bloody" before.'

'How flattering,' said Hilda.

Grania was gazing at College Green. She had forgotten about Burke and Goldsmith, standing in front of the magnificent façade of Trinity. Respect for artists must have ended with the eighteenth century, under the oppressor. Between the statues, undergraduates in duffle-coats stood talking beside a cluster of motor-bikes. The sun was low, and it was cold. Just beyond the adjacent railings about twenty people waited in a bus queue. They were shabby. They looked as if they lived a hard life. They wore poor, far-from-new overcoats. Nobody wore a hat. The women had scarves on their heads. A ragged old man went by with a horse and cart, the horse leaving a deposit on the road. Except for Trinity and the bank, it might have been a poor country town. One felt that the country was close because of the mud on the buses and cars, though perhaps it was merely an absence of pride in material possessions. Large American taxis, very dirty and decrepit, waited at the centre, and their aged drivers stood conversing. But the new cars of foreign make, passing by, were equally filthy. There was a quantity of litter beyond the railings. A bent old sandwich-man went past, advertising 'Amusements' in O'Connell Street. He was followed by a flock of rosy-faced student priests, who looked much more cheerful than everyone else. The sea was close, too, because there were seagulls strutting around the forecourt. Far off, on the other side, she could see the ageless lady with the powerful-lensed spectacles who used to bring an evening paper to the window of the Bentley: still rubbing her mittens together and stamping her feet, still selling true love stories, tales of Hollywood glamour and knitting magazines with terrible patterns, on paper with a pungent smell. 'God,' she thought, 'it's poor, shabby, provincial, lost to the world, decaying and hopeless.'

A sudden shout from the bank made her look the other way.

Dermot stood with an arm round one of the pillars, his spectacles raised on to the top of his bald head, and his right hand covering his eyes.

They sat forward, staring at him in astonishment.

'woe! woe! woe!' he howled, like some wild creature.

They were speechless, until Hilda whispered: 'What's happened? God, what's happened?'

Slowly he released the pillar and, moving away, tried to find the steps below with feeble searching movements of his feet.

He removed his hand from his eyes and, pointing a trembling finger at the sky, bellowed: 'Woe, woe is me! Darkness over all!'

'He's blind!' cried Hilda. 'My God, he's gone blind!'

A seagull went flapping across the steps and shot up into the blue.

'Oedipus Rex,' said Martin dryly. 'The setting is good, but it seems to be his own translation.'

'D'you mean . . . ?' Hilda began.

'apollo! apollo!' roared Dermot, slowly feeling his way across the cobblestones of the forecourt, his arms outstretched, his spectacles glinting in the sunshine like some weird head-dress.

'*Ad majorem Dei gloriam,*' said Martin.

'Wonderful,' said Grania. 'Wonderful.'

'Apollo! Apollo!' howled Dermot. 'Apollo has finished me off!'

He was moving implacably, though with infinite labour, immediately in the direction of two horrified employees in a corner of the forecourt. The one held a mop, and the other a sweeping-brush, with a bucket of water between them.

'Lead me to exile, friends!' roared Dermot.

They backed away. The man holding the mop raised it defensively.

'Take me, friends! Lead me away! Most accursed and wretched of mortals!'

'Easy now, easy now,' warned the man with the mop, lifting it above his head and taking another pace back.

'Who the —— hell are you?' demanded Dermot, quickly bringing his spectacles down on to his nose.

They stared at him.

'Mother a God, what came over you at all?' whispered the man with the brush.

'The Drama!' declared Dermot majestically. 'Have you no appreciation of your surroundings?'

He made a gesture to embrace the surroundings, and found that the entire bus queue had broken line and every face was pressed against the railings. A man held a baby clothed in red high over the top so that it could see everything.

'Men and women of Ireland, awake!' cried Dermot, turning on them. 'Half dead from forty years of self-abuse . . . throw off your CHAINS!'

The crowd, which was rapidly enlarging, pressed closer to the railings. The words 'Dermot Sleator' were to be heard among them. A small boy pressed a hand through with an autograph-book, and a man shouted: 'Give us a song, Dermot!' But to no effect.

'Where are the poachers now?' shouted Dermot. 'The hunts-men and grooms? The live ones? The irrepressibles? Where is Flurry Knox? Where is Phil the Fluter? What's become of Charlie Lever? Where has your gaiety gone? What have you done with JOY?'

Grania was watching in ecstasy. Of course this city was a stage. Unchanging, it was devoted not to progress, but to the eternal human. Now the splendid setting and the ever-ready audience had its flesh-and-blood performer. College Green was complete. Even the seagulls were crying it from the top of the bank.

'Yeh haven't the —— imagination to invent a LIE any more!' thundered Dermot at the silent mob, gazing open-mouthed through the bars.

'Where are the gay inventive spirits that turned misfortune into farce? You look like a funeral, the whole bloody lot of you. But what's become of the WAKE?'

'Ah, give us a song, man!'

'Draw us a pitcher, at any rate,' piped the small boy with the notebook.

'Do your *own* —— work! Come on, let's dance on the coffin!' roared Dermot, breaking into a jig. 'Where's the porther?'

There was a ripple of applause.

'That's more like it, Dermot!'

'Silence!' roared Dermot, coming to a halt and breathing heav-ily. 'Plain people of Ireland, *awake!* That is my final word! You have nothing to lose but your **Virginity!**'

'*He's* a one,' said Flanagan.

chapter twelve

'It's just along here,' said Ann, as they turned into Lower Leeson Street. She was feeling guilty about walking him this distance, although he had taken what she thought exorbitant pleasure in the charms of Stephen's Green.

The houses were elegant. But as they arrived at hers and went up the stone steps Patrick felt a sense of depression at the appearance of the door in need of paint, the cracked pane of glass in the fanlight, and the dirty muslin curtains in the tall ground-floor window which moved aside at the corner to reveal a grey-haired lady staring him in the face. They promptly moved back again and she was invisible. Ann opened the door and they stepped into total darkness and a curious coldness as in some underground cave. They were walking on uncarpeted stone.

'I can't see a thing,' he said, in his blindness. 'Where are you?'

She laughed, and there was an echo.

'I'm terribly sorry, they economise on light-bulbs. I'm up here. Keep close to the wall.'

He placed a hand against the dank wall and edged along it until his foot bumped against the bottom stair.

'Mind the bicycle,' she warned from somewhere above.

'I haven't encountered one.'

She switched on a dim light on an upper landing and he found that he was walking up a threadbare carpet beside a dark brown wall. He put his right hand on the thin wooden bannister. It moved, so he released it. There was now a peculiar smell—whether of cats or cooking he could not be sure. On the landing he was approaching was a window of dark-coloured glass, with an aspidistra set against it. One would certainly have taken these to be poor lodgings. But this was one of Dublin's superior streets, on the 'right side' of the river. He remembered the naïve and charming drawings that used to appear—and perhaps still appeared—in *Dublin Opinion,* featuring elegant ladies and gentlemen returned as ghosts to just such a house; the lady in a long gown, the gentleman leading her by the arm to the ball somewhere upstairs. Heating, lighting and carpeting must have been better then.

Ann had gone on ahead because she could not recall the condition of her room. She was glad that she had done so, since on the divan bed were her pyjamas, an ash-tray full of butts and an open copy of *L'Étranger* by Camus, which might have seemed pretentious. When these had been cleared away the room was tidy. She lit the gas-fire and called out: 'Come on in!'

'This is a surprise,' said Patrick, standing in the doorway.

The room was bright and warm, with pale pink walls and red curtains. Besides the divan there were two big dilapidated and comfortable arm-chairs, a small writing-desk and chair, and a table supporting a record-player.

'All my own work,' she said. 'What did you expect?'

'Well, the approach is a little sordid.'

'You should visit some of the houses on the north side. They've rebuilt whole streets reproducing the Georgian, and already they've got broken windows and scarred doorways, filled with wretched scabby children and ancient prams. New slums for old. I'll put the kettle on. Do sit down.'

She went into the small kitchen.

'You seem to feel strongly about it,' he called out from an arm-chair.

'It's my country,' she replied. 'Yours too, isn't it?'

'Yes. Yes.'

Above the white mantelpiece was a Degas reproduction of ballet dancers, and below it two small Staffordshire dogs, a smaller black elephant, and a framed photograph of Mr and Mrs Neelan many years ago outside a tennis club pavilion, he in long whites, she in a longish skirt, both holding tennis-rackets and looking very happy. Records of Mozart and Frank Sinatra lay beside the record-player. A small crucifix, he noted with surprise and slight shock, was on the wall above the divan. He had entirely forgotten about that Irish division.

'Strictly speaking, I shouldn't really have asked you here, you know,' she called from the kitchen.

'Oh!' he said, looking again at the crucifix. 'Why's that?'

'I'm supposed to be more or less engaged.'

'Really? Who to?'

'His name is Brendan Smith. He's just been called to the Bar.'

'I see.'

'Well, to tell you the truth, I'm being an awful hypocrite, because that's why I asked you here. We couldn't have gone out to tea without half Dublin discussing it.'

'Really?'

'Anyhow, I like to feel my room is being put to some use, and I don't imagine tea is particularly harmful. I'm afraid I'm going to have to give it up. The room, I mean.'

'To get married?'

'No. No,' said Ann, emerging with the tea-tray. 'It was for attending lectures at odd hours of the day. Well, it was for independence, but that was my excuse. But if I get a job here I can easily go in and out with Father, or on the bus. I'm afraid I'll have to put this on the floor. I've never had a table for some reason.'

'That's fine.'

'Alternatively, I might go away. I had thoughts of going to London.'

'These alternatives don't seem to have much to do with marriage.'

'No. No, they don't, do they? I haven't made my mind up. Milk and sugar?'

'Yes, please.'

'It should really be Paris. I did rather well in French. But that seems, somehow, too far. My parents are really very dependent on me. My father goes to London quite a lot, and Mother sometimes too. Besides, I find the idea of London exciting. Have some cake?'

'Thanks.'

She was sitting on the floor in front of the gas-fire, which brought a flush to her face. She was pretty, with a slim figure in her fawn jumper and green tweed skirt. Not only was her dark hair entirely opposite to her mother's, but she appeared to bear no resemblance to either of the people on the mantelpiece, except possibly a liveliness which was, however, more restrained than theirs. Her parents' Dublin accents were more pronounced.

'*I* was rather good at English. Does that mean London should be right for me?' Patrick asked.

'That was at Oxford, wasn't it? Rather different to poor old National. You must have been *very* good.'

'You seem to have an inferiority complex about everything here. What's so exciting about London?'

'Plays, concerts, the chance every day to meet someone new rather than someone you've met a thousand times before. I want to get away from the parish pump.'

'What about Brendan?'

She was gazing at the fire, with one hand held up to it.

'He doesn't.'

They were silent. Patrick ate his cake and drank his tea.

'I've rather blotted my copy-book with Brendan,' she said, smiling. 'Temporarily, I hope. We've Father Hanna—whom doubtless you haven't met—out in the mountains. He came to dinner and was so damn smug I couldn't restrain myself. He disapproves of the outer world. Only Ireland is virtuous, and must be kept that way by authority. Brendan was horrified, and he's so kind and good-natured that I've felt very ashamed of myself ever since. He's very intelligent, in his way. I gather he's brilliant at law.'

'I see.'

She glanced at him.

'I put that badly. You don't really see at all. I also protested,' she added, 'at the idea of destroying your lovely house.'

'So you know about that?'

'Yes. Does your grandfather really mean to sell? I'm not spying.'

'He does. Unless we can think of an alternative.'

'What sort of alternatives are there?'

'I don't know. I've hardly slept for a week, thinking about it. My mother and my mad aunt, Delia, are in a way more involved than I. They would have to stop their incredible extravagances, and I'm afraid they're both too set in their extraordinary ways.'

'She's very beautiful.'

'Did you think so?'

'Of course. What a figure! How does she do it?'

'I don't know. Yours is pretty good too.'

'Is it?' She looked at him and added quickly: 'I'm a little younger. Do you want some more tea?'

'No, thanks.'

'I'll clear these things away.'

'I'll help you wash up.'

'No, no. I'll only be a second.'

She went to the kitchen, and after a moment he walked to the window and looked out. It was beginning to get dark. The street was quiet. Cars went past now and then, but mostly he could hear the footsteps of the passers-by. The world seemed forgotten. The houses gave the sensation of antiquity and timelessness, and indeed he had no notion of what time it was and glanced at his watch to discover. It was four o'clock.

'What could you do here?' asked Ann, coming out of the kitchen.

'I was just thinking that the temptation to do anything here must be extremely slight.'

'Did you get that by looking out of the window?'

'Yes. Silly, I'm afraid.'

'Not at all. It's true. Come and sit down. It's getting cold.'

They sat before the fire, and he produced cigarettes. It was getting dark.

'What about your father's shop? I often walk past the window in Suffolk Street, with the guns and rods and that old salmon in the glass case, and think it's about the most pleasant and dignified shop in Dublin.'

'I must tell him. I believe business has improved since they started flying in all the anglers from the English midlands. Our new industry. We've a smaller shop in Galway too, you know. But it's really the family investments that have kept us going. There's not much to do. My grandfather himself only spends a brief day now, upstairs in the office. There are two able assistants, and another, the gardener's son, Mick Trench, who's only there out of charity.'

'What about your land?'

'Yes, that's the more likely possibility. One would have to get rid of our Mr Duffy. But then again I know very little about farming.'

'You'd need an expert to help you. Daddy's mad on pigs at the moment, but he's always talking about starting a market garden. Why don't you do that, before he does?—though I shouldn't be saying it. You have contracts with Dublin hotels and restaurants, and your fortune is made.'

'That had occurred to me.'

'Daddy might advise you. To be honest, I think he's lost interest. He's very busy. Oh dear, I've said the wrong thing.'

'Never mind. Where does he have his office, by the way?'

'Dame Street. The same place was used as a wholesale department for curtains, and then as the city office for some new cement works.'

'He told me about that.'

'I expect he talked your head off on the plane?'

'No, not at all, he was very entertaining.'

'He's not a bad sort. I expect your father thinks he's a schemer, but he's really quite naïve. Maybe he's a different person when he's at work. He's brought off some surprising *coups*. But there I go again. . . . What kind of a job was it you had in London?'

'Advertising. I quit. A soulless task, as everybody's been told in every book written about it. Unfortunately I was doing it quite well. If we can't think of any solution for Edenmore I suppose I'll have to go back to it. But I didn't come here because of that. I came because of Dublin. It seems so human and real after London. Yet I don't know about living here all the time.'

'I know, well enough. Where did you live there?'

'In a flat in Knightsbridge, with my mother, a horror called Flanagan, and a resident cook called Charlotte. Luckily I had my own room upstairs. My mother seems to have no discrimination about people, from those that run charity balls to sculptors from Chelsea.'

'How exciting.'

'Are you mad?'

'And what are the girls like? I don't just mean the Chelsea girls.'

'They're the same as the others. Full of pretensions and the platitudes of the moment.'

'And Irish girls are different?'

'Yes. Like you.'

'Ah, go on with you!'

'We've been talking naturally.'

'Yes. Perhaps it's your doing. The gentlemen I've been used to are very gauche and rough.'

'You're exaggerating.'

'The amount of college dances at which I've had stout poured down my front! It was wonderful to meet Brendan and find he didn't drink or dance. I suppose Oxford puts the polish on?'

'You're making a mock of me now.'

'Oh, I wouldn't dream of it!'

They laughed.

'Of course, my parents think London is a young girl's ruin. Pagan and immoral.'

'Are you a good Catholic?'

'I am, of course! You're one of the pagans, I presume?'

'I am of course.'

'And tell me, is it true that everyone there sleeps with everyone else, as they tell us in the novels?'

'Not quite. Only the Protestants.'

'You haven't been reading Graham Greene lately.'

'That's with a sense of sin. It's different. What are *you* doing with those heretical French novels that I noticed earlier in the bookshelf?'

'I was interested.'

'I thought it wasn't allowed?'

'Not by Father Hanna. But he's not the final judge. They say English Catholicism is different. Mother has found out that Hugo Lorrimer is one, and she's all agog to meet him. Are you going to the play?'

'No. Mother's going. I'm keeping my grandfather company. I really must ring him up now. It's getting late.'

'It's well for you, to have seen *too* many plays! Brendan won't come, and Daddy won't either. Only the women here seem to have kept an interest in things. Norah Gerraty's coming with us. I'm quite excited, I don't mind admitting. He's had a great presence in the films I've seen. Always very grand parts, but I gather he's not a bit grand in this. A play of the "new school". You can't imagine how it's like food for starving people over here.'

'You've persuaded me of that. Wherabouts is the phone?'

'Out on the landing. I'll show you.'

He did not want to leave. There seemed to be much more to say. He had a feeling that their conversation had been abrupt, because they were in a hurry to speak about everything: not a coldness but a compatibility.

The landing was totally dark. She was wearing perfume. He put out a hand and touched her shoulder.

'Sorry. I can't see a damn thing.'

'There's a light somewhere. I ought to know it by now. There we are!'

A very small light came on above the phone-box.

'Have you some pennies?'

'Yes, I think so.'

She left him, and in a moment his grandfather's voice was at the other end, sad, apprehensive, and loud enough to travel from Suffolk Street without any wires.

'Is that you, Patrick?'

'Yes, it is. When will you be ready to go home?'

'Well, in a quarter of an hour or so. But I can come and collect you. Where are you?'

'No, no. Don't bother. I'll be there.'

'All right then.'

She had pulled the curtains and switched on a yellow lamp, making the room very bright and warm.

'We must meet again, Ann,' he said.

She was looking down at the fire. She turned to him and in a quiet and rather tense way, replied: 'I'm sorry. I don't really think we should.'

'You what?'

'I don't think we should. I'll see you in London maybe,' she added smiling. 'Things are different there.'

'But this is ridiculous.'

'No, it's not. Come on, I'll show you down the stairs. You'd never manage the lights.'

They descended, through occasional dim patches of light, without speaking. This time he saw the very muddy bicycle in the hall. She opened the door and said: 'Good luck with your big decision. We all seem to be at the cross-roads, don't we?'

'Yes. We do.'

'The moment of choice. Good-bye. Thanks for coming.'

They shook hands.

'Thanks for having me. But this is rather extreme, isn't it?'

'No. Not really. Go along. I've left you with quite a walk, I'm afraid.'

'All right. But I think you're mad.'

'Maybe so.'

'Good-bye.'

'Good-bye.'

He went down the steps and set off along Leeson Street without turning back, at first in confusion and then in anger.

chapter thirteen

The Major cautiously descended the old curving staircase, looking dapper in his grey business suit. He was feeling tired. The day was a daze of O'Briens, Murphys, McGraths, Maguires, Dohertys and Fogartys. He had passed the afternoon not at the shop, but at a meeting of shopkeepers to consider street decorations for Christmas. They had decided on a display of very meagre bunting after a discussion sufficiently long to permit everyone to express his individuality. The Major found the ordinariness of ordinary people, intensified by the native parochialism, extremely wearisome. They found him entertaining, eccentric, and a little alarming. Indeed, he feared now that he had overdone it with his suggestion that Mrs O'Brien could give them invaluable advice on bunting if her costume at the last Phœnix Park races was anything to go by.

The shop below presented an agreeable sight, with guns and fishing-rods against the oak-panelled walls, a display of highly polished saddles and stirrups and other equestriana, and two glass cases containing fishing equipment. Mr Flynn, an assistant of many years' service, was showing flies to an elderly gentleman in a tweed overcoat whom the Major did not recognise. Mr Gahan, his junior of almost equal long-standing, was helping a woman whom the Major did know, the wife of a well-known trainer, into one of their small range of suede, fur-lined 'country' overcoats.

'You'd want to watch the lady's credit, Mr Gahan,' he said gloomily, 'after the last meeting at Baldoyle.'

Mr Gahan smiled, and the lady took his point delightedly with: 'Oh, you shocking man! We're not all heavy gamblers like you. You just wait till Leopardstown.'

'Which of your ancient nags are you running there?'

'I'm not saying. You don't deserve it. Will you be going?'

'I might. If you'll be wearing that handsome coat.'

'Oh, you devil! All right. It's a bargain. Buy me a drink before the first race and I'll tell you something that'll make it worth your while. See you in the bar.'

'I'm afraid I'm rather past all that.'

'Ah, go on, you don't look a day over forty. We'll be there, anyhow. Don't forget. Promise now.'

'Very well.'

'I hear Grania's over.'

'Yes. Yes, she is.'

'Give her my love,' she said, rather uncertainly.

'I will if I see her.'

Mick Trench was standing at the glass entrance door, cleaning his nails. He wore an ordinary tie instead of his evening version, and ordinary shoes, but his suit was the same, and his sideburns, and they were ill-adapted to these premises.

'Have you nothing better to do, Trench?'

'No.'

'I feel sure you can find something. You won't be here much longer if you don't pull your weight, you know.'

'I won't be here much longer in any case.'

'Oh! Really? Is your father aware of this?'

'He is.'

'Where do you propose to go?'

'Liverpool.'

'Gracious me! What for?'

'Life.'

The Major quickly stepped outside, to hide his smile. He was rather pleased. There was still some virtue in the native responses, even from this most unlikely quarter. All the same, Trench would be lonely. He walked along to Grafton Street to buy an evening paper, intending to read it in the car. He looked forward to the sporting pages. It was dark and cold and noisy with the beginning of the rush-hour traffic. A man in rags, bawling '*Heggal* or *Mail* or *Press!*' ceased for a moment to give him his change at great speed. He moved away and saw Norah Gerraty approaching rapidly under the nearest lamplight.

'Who are *you* hurrying to?' he inquired. 'He must be a gentleman of considerable appeal. I thought you were going to knock me over.'

She was nearly one foot taller than the Major.

'He's a foreign count,' she replied, with no recollection of where the notion came from. 'He's rolling in wealth. Owns half Europe. D'you think I'd make a countess?'

'I've no doubt of it.'

'Ah, go on! Listen, kidding apart, I'm delighted to meet you. My husband says I'm to be nice to you.'

'How very strange and convenient for us both.'

'Isn't it now! But sure I never see you except at the races. Look, we're having a house-warming next week. On Sunday at six. Will you come along?'

'I doubt it very much. I haven't been to a party since 1928, when an ambassador asked me to leave his house.'

'Ah do! It'd do you good.'

'It would bring me to the grave. I've one foot there already.'

'Stuff and nonsense. Will you ask the family, anyhow? I hear they're over.'

She suddenly remembered that the count was Grania's. Why was it on her mind?'

'I don't imagine they'll hesitate. I wouldn't come with them in any case. They cramp my style.'

'We'd find a corner to ourselves somewhere.'

'Your husband seems amenable. What's it all about?'

'I think you'll find out when you get home. You'll have a dark visitor.'

'Not you?'

'No, no. You make me laugh! It's good for me. We should have a chat more often.'

'I see you're following instructions. I must go. My grandson's meeting me.'

'Tell him about the party.'

'He's a bit old for you.'

'Tch, tch. You're incorrigible! 'Bye now.'

'Good-bye.'

Walking back, he reflected that the tendency for Irish women of a certain age—Catholics always, not the Protestant ladies on committees—to be flirtatious was quite entertaining. They were infinitely more alive than their husbands. After five minutes, certainly, it would become intolerable. But, behind all the chatter, this one had a curious sense of calm and poise about her; something feminine. She was probably capable of silence.

Returning, he sat in the Vauxhall in the small car park, put on the light, and lighting also his pipe opened his paper on the steering-wheel and read: 'A 62-year-old Co. Galway farmer died yesterday, having taken a preparation for foot rot in sheep, under the impression that it was whisky.'

He had a return of the slight nausea which had been afflicting him lately. Opening out the inner pages, he read under Entertainments: *'The Kiss of Death.* Hugo Lorrimer takes a part out of the ordinary in this pre-London production opening tonight. Irish film fans who have given him plaudits as a corpulent but elegant figure in such costume hits as *Witty but Nice, Gaiety Girls,* and *Good King Charles,* are due for some lifting of the eyebrows! The play is a first effort by a young Mancunian, Tom Tooley. Another Irishman? We were unable to ask him. He works as a building labourer and his employers would not give him time off for the journey. The play is a slashing attack on the parents of today—in Britain—who give their children the Kiss of Death. Lorrimer plays the father. One hopes that it will be understandable to our own audiences. At least we are assured of lively theatre and robust dialogue in the contemporary manner.'

It sounded utterly worthless, the Major thought, but it might have been amusing to take the Gerraty woman to dinner at the Russell and a box, and explode a little of the Catholicism out of her. It was twenty years since anybody had asked him if he wanted to go to the theatre.

He must finish his own piece of journalism, 'Factories or Farms'; give it the final polish tonight. Not a single reader would have the faintest awareness of its hidden prose rhythms, let alone understanding its content. Still, there were odd birds about the country who cultivated their gardens and themselves, and watched the world. One or two might read it. They occasionally wrote letters to the *Irish Times* from Sneem and Ballinscorthy, correcting misapprehensions about the social status of the Copt in present-day Egypt.

Patrick appeared and sat beside him, with apologies for keeping him waiting. His anger had diminished to sadness, and even that was touched with the expectation that he was not going to leave the afternoon's events without a sequel.

The Major put his paper away and drove off, pressing a shilling into the dirty hand of the ancient attendant who came hurrying to the window.

'I was reading about the play,' he said. 'It sounds ghastly.'

'Oh. Perhaps it's powerful. I'm sure they'll say it has "strength and vitality".'

'Like Sleator's pictures? Did you see them?'

'Yes. They had vitality, I thought.'

They turned into Camden Street where the bright shops were staying open and poverty walked abroad. An old woman in rags, talking loudly to herself, crossed the street immediately in front of the car.

'Vitality of the imagination is the important thing,' said the Major, recovering from this shock. 'Bawling and shouting is intolerable without it. I haven't been to a play in thirty years, but I assume them to be afflicted with total poverty of language. Synge said that on the stage one must have joy and reality. That's almost entirely gone now. He derived it from listening through a chink in the floor to the servants in the kitchen. I needn't tell you how little he'd derive from listening to the servants in *our* kitchen.'

'I suppose not.'

A horse and cart were restricting their progress to five miles an hour. Patrick found his concentration disturbed by the recollection of Ann Neelan, and wondered vaguely why ideas, no matter how interesting, always gave place to feelings, no matter how incipient.

The Major was talking:

'In England it's utterly departed. Synge points out that in the other Elizabethan Age the dramatist sat down and repeated striking phrases that he might have heard at dinner with his own family. No. Vitality is dead in the West. Young Trench's taper suit is an apt symbol. Decaying civilisations have always preened themselves. He's going to England, by the way.'

'Really?'

'Yes, to Liverpool. For life.'

They were crossing Portobello Bridge. A red neon sign on top of some garage was reflected in the dark, sad canal.

'I sometimes have a peculiar feeling that we're not all as different as we imagine,' said Patrick. 'Sleator would probably agree with what you've been saying, and I suppose I've been to England for life too. If only we could come together. Mother and Mrs Neelan had another unhappy encounter at the exhibition.'

'All that Irish showing off is an unbearable imposture. As for Trench, these journeys are only meaningful if you have what Keats called an experiencing nature.'

A flurry of cyclists on their way home were crossing themselves as they passed the Rathmines church.

'But the vast majority in this dying civilisation, out of a fever to be entertained in their vacant selves, are turning the world into a conglomeration of squalid cities. I don't know who will succeed us. I suppose the African people. They have vitality.'

'They dress to the nines, when they dress at all,' said Patrick.

'Yes, but for the right reason. It's like drinking because you're happy rather than drinking because you're not.'

'Does simple vigour make a civilisation?'

'Vitality of the imagination is certain to go with it, as in Synge's servant-girls. Why do you want us to be the same, by the way?'

'I don't. I put it badly. I meant that we are, basically: hopes and fears and feelings, and so on.'

'I gave them up many years ago,' said the Major.

They were waiting at the lights in Rathmines.

'Feelings are destructive. If your mother knew that she wouldn't have been wasting her life.'

'She may well agree with you,' said Patrick.

'Perhaps now, though I doubt it. Age is something we all share too. You're prepared for feelings. Others are past them. Rather quickly in Dublin, I'd say. Doubtless marriages are disturbed here, but only by restlessness. Even in London people grow older. Personally I'm only interested in the rarer qualities that distinguish us.'

They were quiet, driving towards the mountains. Patrick felt in a mood to confide. They had never spoken together for so long.

'Mother had a friend called André. Did she tell you?'

'No.'

'I don't know him. He's a foreign count or something.'

'They seem to be in heavy demand all of a sudden.'

'He's disappeared. I think it hurt her a lot. She's not as invulnerable as I was claiming. He never came to the flat, because he disliked her friends.'

'He sounds an improvement.'

'They went to Cannes together.'

'I hope he paid. If he didn't I shall soon hear it from our solicitors.'

'He's very keen on horses, apparently.'

The street-lights were becoming scarcer as they left the city behind.

'What I should have done was to start a riding-school,' said the Major. 'That was reality. Competitively, as an individual, it was most expensive, I'm afraid. Unfortunately our army jumps for our country, and I was the wrong sort of major.'

'Why did you speak of the sea?'

'When?'

'You said it was the only thing you'd missed.'

'Well, it's similar. I'd keep a boat of some sort. You can see it in the people who do these things, and hear it in their speech: the old salts you'll meet out in the West. Untouched by the urban plague.'

'I think you're a bit of a romantic, Grandfather.'

'Against all the evidence, you mean? Perhaps so. I certainly was at one time. So was your grandmother. It destroyed her, poor woman. A romantic realist. The modern distinction of introvert and extrovert has always interested me. I have perhaps the introvert's admiration for the extrovert and his ways.'

The street-lights were perversely returning again, in front of the high stone walls and the bare trees. It was a preparation for Mr Neelan's estate.

'Is this lady whom you all address as Hilda intending a long stay?'

'I think probably till after Christmas.'

'She seems to be rather heavy on the gin.'

'I'm afraid that must be all of us.'

The houses were appearing.

'I wish to God there was another route,' said the Major.

He had spoken almost with a note of amusement. The conversation had somehow pleased him, Patrick thought.

As they left the house behind and were driving in darkness again, he said: 'Someone was telling me that Neelan had the notion of starting a market-garden. Would that be a possibility for us—or for me, rather?'

'A typically gimcrack Neelan idea. More people have been

destroyed by market-gardens in this country than by any other single occupation.'

'You do have a reputation for pessimism, Grandfather.'

'In other countries it's called realism. No one knows what it is here. That's why Ireland is headed for economic ruin. It's also why if Neelan doesn't purchase I'm very doubtful if anyone else will. No one has any money here. Houses of this size have been advertised in the *Irish Times* for years. I think I'll have to settle with Neelan.'

This was said most unhappily.

'Are there any prospects in advertising here?'

'Possibly. But you'd find the company dull.'

'Are you sure?'

'Pretty sure.'

The wall of Edenmore and its beech trees were on the left.

'I met that Gerraty woman in the street and she said that we were to expect a dark visitor. I can't imagine what she was blathering about. Oh, by the way, you're all invited to her house-warming next week. On Sunday at six.'

They turned in the gate, and the headlights at once picked out a couple embracing in the rhododendrons. They broke apart in alarm, and the man quickly pulled the girl deeper into the bushes as the car went past.

'That was Finola,' said Patrick.

'Yes, and I think Paddy, the farm boy,' said the Major. 'I'm glad to see that youth still enjoys the traditional pleasures in Ireland. It's quite surprising.'

They left the car in the garage. Walking in darkness across the yard, Patrick heard the Major say quietly: 'It was pleasant to have someone to talk to.' As they came into the sitting-room, perhaps to remove the impression that anything had been said, the Major added: 'I hope the priest doesn't put a stop to that romance.'

Father Hanna was standing with his back to the mantelpiece. He had heard, but only confusedly. He had been left alone by

Finola some time before and had become apprehensive. It was partly because he had come with a mission. But also the house had disturbed him. This was where they held the pagan rites, in Horse Show Week, that were the scandal of his parish. If his mission succeeded the house would have to be blessed immediately. The faded chintz and the blazing coal fire looked homely and innocent enough, but he had walked along the glass-fronted bookcases and knew better: Oliver Goldsmith, Richard Brinsley Sheridan, Bernard Shaw, Oscar Wilde, George Moore, J. M. Synge, Sean O'Casey, A. E., W. B. Yeats, James Stephens, Percy French, L. A. G. Strong, Lady Gregory, Lord Dunsany, George Berkeley, Edmund Burke, Tom Moore, Charles Lever, Maria Edgeworth, Dean Swift, Samuel Beckett and Somerville and Ross—every single one of them a Protestant! The painting over the mantelpiece was by Jack Yeats, and the brother, W.B., was represented again in a drawing by Augustus John, who was also responsible for a head of James Joyce, a defaulter and the author of an obscene work. Some of the metropolitan priests accepted, and even revered, these names. Father Hanna came from a very rural area and did not. Finola, whose presence had increased his discomfort, had suggested that he 'help himself', but though he felt like a drink he thought it might give a bad impression. She was a pert girl who needed watching, as she was very likely on the way to committing mortal sin.

'Well, well. Father Hanna, I believe,' said the Major. 'Good evening. Can I offer you a drink?'

'How do you do? Ah, I might have a small Irish, thank you.'

The Major went to the old desk in the corner, and having noted the red face with the knobby nose and pock-marks under the white cropped head, thought it safe to give him a large one. He did the same for Patrick and himself.

'Do sit down. This is an unusual pleasure.'

He believed in what used to be called politeness, and remembered that they all addressed him as 'Father', but he found that he could not make this descent.

They sat before the fire, the Major noting sadly that Finola had cast several months' coal supply on to it.

'Your girl showed me in. I apologise. I thought you came home earlier. You've passed me many times on the road.'

'You are observant. I usually do. There was a meeting today.'

'And I delayed him,' added Patrick, smiling at the priest. He felt that he should add his friendly quota to this curious meeting.

'Do you mind if I smoke a pipe?'

'Not at all. I will myself,' replied the Major. 'This is an unusual honour,' he continued as the priest lit up. He could not imagine what was coming. His only guess was that they were hoping for a death-bed conversion and it made him most uneasy.

'I understand you're contemplating selling this beautiful house,' said Father Hanna, releasing a cloud of pungent smoke that entirely obscured the Jack Yeats.

'That is so,' replied the Major, after a moment. 'Do you know of a prospective purchaser?'

'I've been asked to speak for one.' He looked at the Major mysteriously through the smoke.

'Who is it?'

'One of our religious orders.'

'Good God.'

'Ahem!' said Father Hanna, glancing into the fire. 'They are hoping to have a novitiate in my parish.'

'I see. I see. What a curious alternative.'

'Alternative?'

'I mean, there is another interested party.'

'Ah yes, Tom Neelan. I know about that.'

'Oh you do?'

'Ours is, if I may say so, a more attractive and worthwhile proposition. Neelan would pull the house to the ground. We'd add to it, very considerably. We've got a big modern design out, from Charlie Gerraty.'

'I understand.'

'Powerful and contemporary. Nothing gimcrack. I have to visit those Neelan houses down below, and I can tell you this, I don't know what's going to happen when it rains.'

The Major went and poured himself another drink, with Patrick watching him and Father Hanna watching the fire.

'It's curious. It reminds one of Ibsen,' said the Major. 'You've read him?'

'No, I can't say I have. Now I'm not here to discuss . . .'

'Churches, or homes for the people, I mean.'

'A novitiate's not a church,' said Father Hanna, quite sharply. 'A home for student priests, if you want to talk about homes.'

'It's the same thing,' said the Major, who was becoming excited in his own way. 'Personally I've always preferred *Peer Gynt* and *Brand*. When the imagination is replaced by the drawing-room and the problems of the housewife, I lose interest. However, Ibsen's churches were loftier than yours, if I may say so, and an appreciation of *Peer Gynt* does not particularly dispose me towards a novitiate.'

'I'm afraid I don't follow you.'

'Aren't there enough novitiates around? Half the youth of Ireland seems to be walking the roads here in celibate costume.'

'I don't like your tone, I'm afraid,' said Father Hanna, putting his glass down in the grate. 'They are giving themselves to God's service, and have been called by Him, in person.'

'To be quite frank,' said the Major, who was standing behind his own chair, 'your proposition makes me shiver.' The Major shivered and some of his drink spilled on the carpet. 'That this house should be destroyed may be tolerable. That it should have vile modern additions is utterly out of the question.'

'Very well then,' said Father Hanna, angrily rising, infected by the Major's impassioned appearance. 'The Fathers would have given you the price, believe you me! Fifteen thousand pounds, I understand.'

'Oh, so you know about that too?'

'I'll take my leave of you.'

'Don't be silly, man. Sit down.'

'I'm not accustomed to being spoken to like that!'

'Doubtless not.'

'I'm to tell them it's out of the question. Is that correct?'

'It is.'

'Very well then. Good-bye to you.'

'I'll see you out,' murmured Patrick.

'I know my way,' said Father Hanna, departing into the hall and shutting the door hard.

'That was quick,' said Patrick after a moment.

The Major was wearily rubbing his hand over his eyes and forehead.

'I shouldn't have lost my temper,' he said. 'The poor man was doing his job. I'll write to Neelan tonight. We'd better get this over. It's been going on long enough.'

Father Hanna collected his black hat, black gaberdine and big stick, and hurried out of the house, only just avoiding collision with the suit of armour. Striding down the avenue, he heard a movement in the rhododendrons and instinctively lashed out with his stick. It landed low on Finola Doyle who was facing the other way. She screamed. It was a high prolonged shriek that might have come from some wild bird. Father Hanna uttered a gasp of horror and astonishment. 'Ow! Ow!' cried Finola. The lovers were dimly visible, because the drawing-room curtains had been pulled aside and Patrick and the Major were peering out. 'Ha, ha,' said Father Hanna. 'So I've caught you in the act!'

'You've hurt her,' shouted Paddy. 'What the hell do you think you're doing?'

'How dare you speak to me like that! Out of this, you. Off home, now! I'll see you later.'

'You old brute,' said Finola, rubbing her injury.

'What! Listen to me, my girl. You're in very serious trouble. You both are. If you want absolution . . .'

'We don't want anything,' said Paddy. 'We've had enough. We're going away.'

'To England!' shouted Finola, recovering.

'I might have guessed it,' said Father Hanna. 'You'll have fit company there, all right! But you'll hear from me before you go!'

'I'll sue you,' said Finola, 'I'll sue you. We'll have you in the courts.'

'Assault and battery,' shouted Paddy.

'That's enough now! You'll hear more of this.'

Father Hanna waved his stick and strode away. The Major's overheard remark suddenly made sense and he felt himself turning scarlet. This was what happened when young girls took employment in Protestant houses, especially in this house.

Mr Trench, also roused by the din, was standing in the doorway of the gate-lodge with the light behind him.

'Father, do you mind if I have a word with you?'

'What the devil's the matter with *you?*'

'Could you come inside a moment, Father?'

'What do you want, damn you? Oh, very well. But I haven't long. I've things to do.'

They went inside.

chapter fourteen

Hugo Lorrimer sat before the cracked mirror in a dressing-room that had seen better days, when Henry Irving sat in it. He was altering his make-up to express the ravages of parenthood required for Act Three. It was the second interval. He had begun as a rubicund Manchester tycoon, healthy enough to tyrannise his over-refined wife and drive his unwilling son through the family business. In Act Two, however, the scene had shifted from his prosperous villa residence to Shank Lane whence his son, Frederick, had fled. There he was known as Fred, and worse still was living with a Nigerian girl named Honoria. In the person of Alfred Higgins—never known as Alf—he had paid a violent visit and persuaded his son to return home. (In fact, it was the reported grief of his delicate wife that had done this.) He was now, or ought to be, pale and suddenly ageing. Lorrimer was vaguely grieved to find that this was achieved by removing his make-up and adding very little. He liked his face, however. With his aquiline nose and strong chin he had very nearly been a matinée idol, but something indefinable was missing, and also he had become portly—and distinguished—at an early age.

He was apprehensive. It was impossible to tell how it was going. The applause had been sparse. The audience had been remarkably silent, and he was well aware that this city conducted a great deal of its history in the theatre. *The Playboy of the Western World* had provoked a riot, and Sean O'Casey's works had more than once been the cause of similar strife. He himself was being rather naughty, as he would term it, and was seeking personal popularity by playing a rôle exactly opposite to that intended by the author, who was happily absent. He had not done so in Manchester, but having been assisted to the Faith in Belgravia by Father Adolphus he felt a strange affection for Ireland, a country he had never visited before, and desired to be liked and accepted. Hence by inflections of the voice he had until now been presenting Alfred Higgins not as an explosive bully but as a wise and amusing gentleman faced with a dim-witted son. He had very nearly said 'dear boy' once or twice, which was not in the script and would scarcely have suited a Manchester tycoon.

The performance he had chosen, he would frankly have admitted, suited him far better. The rôle had first been offered to Sir Donald Wolfit, who would doubtless have been splendidly apoplectic but had considered it an inferior play. Lorrimer was not accustomed to being the second choice, and this eased his conscience. At the same time he felt no guilt at all about taking the rôle of hero away from the surprised Jeremy Coffey who was playing Frederick—and very suitably too, since he was callow, unwashed and probably a Communist.

They were now, however, approaching the final major scene and Fred's big speech, in which he finds the courage to condemn his father. Lorrimer felt himself compelled to revert to the author's purpose, since his own share consisted of the twice-repeated interjection: 'Christ!' and thirdly: 'Christ, I'm going to kill you!' and a witty inflection in these circumstances was scarcely possible. On the third exclamation he would lunge forward, suffer a heart attack, and die. Having worked the audience to his side for two acts, he was confident that he would not die as the villain of the piece. He would rise and bow, with his popularity greatly enhanced.

His popularity in this city had already surprised and delighted him. Reporters had met him at the airport, pursued him to the Shelbourne Hotel, and incessantly interviewed him. It was delightful but testing. Many questions had required evasion, since everything was so curiously unwell at home.

His wife was making a reputation with acidly witty novels exposing the shallow futility of people in Chelsea. What puzzled him was that these same people were her chosen companions almost exclusive of the rest of the human species. What was particularly relevant at the moment, however, was that her latest novel, which he had come across in proof copy in their Chelsea house, not only took the lid off the author's chosen companions once more, but featured a heavily built actor who was portentous and a sybarite. It was due for publication before Christmas, and the only very slender protection was that his wife wrote under her own name.

It was also curious that their neighbours were taken to task for living in squalor, whereas the actor, on the contrary, was ridiculed for having rather lovely things about the house, his bachelor residence. It was plainly their own marital residence, much of the furnishings, including the joss sticks, the black and gold curtains, and the plaster bambini flying around the candelabra being described with precision. In fact, these objects had been as much her choice as his own. Even the jewelled crucifix, on which she had expended a scarifying paragraph, had been approved by her, as had his conversion. Misguidedly, though flatteringly, she had considered it romantic and fashionable, and had boasted of it everywhere, even in Chelsea; although it was true that she herself had not been persuaded, or had even attempted, to see the light. It would almost certainly in any case have been futile. He could never have explained to her how Father Adolphus had, over brandy and cigars, through many nights, offered him a source of consolation and appealed to his love of ceremony. He had sat with his hands folded on his bright check waistcoat and dreamed of the splendours of Rome and sometimes of himself in rich ecclesiastical garb. Father Adolphus, the historian of the Benedictine Order, was profoundly versed in theological doctrine and in the varying merits of liqueurs and vintage wines.

The journalists had not been Lorrimer's only followers in Dublin. On the table before him was a letter delivered at the theatre that evening from an entirely unknown woman signing herself Norah Gerraty; and there had been other approaches. He had received about a dozen phone-calls and letters at the Shel-

bourne, largely from ladies, inviting him to lunch or tea. Miss—
or Mrs—Gerraty's invitation was to come for drinks with some
friends after the show. He would do so happily. He would take
great pleasure in evading the rest of the cast, who varied from
Nigerians to Jeremy Coffey and dear old May Platt who should
have been a vicar's wife and was aptly suited to the rôle of Mrs
Higgins. As an actress she was less well suited, since she had been
out of work for many years, and was alarmingly lacking in confidence. She also considered the play 'too strong'. It was certainly
strong, and bore no resemblance to any of Lorrimer's previous
undertakings, but if this was what people wanted *he* was not
going to sit in the Garrick and dream of days gone by.

Also at his elbow was a note from Grania, reading: 'Best of
luck, darling. Will be round to see you.' He had always considered Grania adorable, but he could see her in London. He felt
that he was here to meet new people, and particularly members
of his new-found faith. But he would certainly welcome and en-
tertain her. The management had been confusingly generous in
depositing two bottles of whisky in the room, with a remarkable
number of glasses. It made one slightly anxious as to what was
anticipated.

A youth opened the door and informed him in an almost incomprehensible dialect that the curtain was about to rise.

He was not required at once, but after a final examination in
the mirror he went out and stood in the wings, in the Manchester
business suit that was so dreary when one was accustomed to
period costume.

The sub-plot was working itself out. His 'wife' was treating
one of the firm's former executives to an evening cocktail, while
she consumed tomato juice. This gentleman had been eased out
of the business by Alfred Higgins, was in dire straits and had
come to ask for mercy. On finding that Alfred Higgins had not
yet returned, he was discovering, by means of rather elusive
questions, that Mrs Higgins had been browbeaten all her sad life.
There was a faint suggestion of mutual attraction. The room was

elegant. Mr Higgins was presented as a self-made man who had learned to purchase articles of taste; as for example the Chippendale furniture and the Chelsea figurines on the mantelpiece. Like Lorrimer's wife, the author believed that this was a form of condemnation.

Lorrimer caught glimpses of the audience: extremely attentive, he thought, but curiously stern in expression.

On cue, he entered the hall, deposited brief-case and bowler, stepped down into the room and exclaimed, to a really objectionable actor named Vincent Hillyard: 'Jackson! What the devil are you doing here?'

A lengthy passage-at-arms ensued, witnessed by Mrs Higgins in alarm, until at last Jackson departed. Mrs Higgins was then taken to task—wittily by Lorrimer—for attempting Jackson's defence, and questions as to why the son had not returned from the factory, where he was 'working his way up', were resolved by his arrival, intoxicated but very coherent.

Jeremy Coffey's eyes blazed. He was a sickly youth with long hair, and an over-emphatic performer. He had been called suddenly to Shank Lane. Honoria was going to have a baby. Mrs Higgins wept. Mr Higgins became apoplectic. Lorrimer had to say repeatedly: 'You're no damn good, and you never were,' which pleased him because they were the only words he could produce in a Manchester accent. A long speech followed from Fred, explaining how his father was responsible for destroying his life. He had taught him that he must charm people, get on, financially succeed by all means possible. At the age of ten, when he had been sent home from school in disgrace for stealing a stamp and was lying in bed in misery, his father had come upstairs and kissed him. 'It should have been *you*, Mother!' he shouted. 'It should have been *you!*'

Now they were approaching the big closing scene. Fred made his appeal. 'Listen, Father,' he said, almost tenderly, 'I'm going back to Shank Lane . . .'

'You're what?'

'Listen, Father, you've got to listen. Sit down. Sit down.'

Lorrimer sat down, livid and spluttering as Sir Donald might have managed it.

'You've got to *understand*. Let me describe Shank Lane to you. Oh God, how can I begin? Well, for a start, it's alive, it's really, humanly, vitally, alive. Do you understand what I mean, Father? Oh yes, I know, you came. But you didn't look about you, not with understanding. You didn't *look* at Honoria. You didn't look at Alice. She is a whore, yes, all right, but she is a person, and a person with a heart. Terry is a pimp, but he loves her, and he is my *friend*. They are the richer ones, and they live richly too. They don't spend it on all this junk—antique furniture, pottery, paintings, *books*. They don't read. They live! But they *all* live richly. You'll even find a mother and daughter sharing the same man, as friends. Does that shock you? It's living, I tell you, Father. And when they speak, it's from the heart. By God, how they speak! If only you could hear them. It's rich and real. None of your decadent eloquence. No word with more than four letters, and they say them over and over again. That was enough at the beginning. It's enough now. But oh—how can you who are forging the armaments and the bombs understand such a life?'

'I make textiles,' said Lorrimer, as humorously as he could contrive it, forgetting about Sir Donald, though once again consciously holding back the words 'dear boy'.

'Oh no you don't!'

'I can only assure you . . .'

(It was his last opportunity.)

'No, no, you don't. I'll tell you what happens then, Father. You and your kind arrive, knocking at the doors saying: "Come with us, join the racket, we're all in it, boys, together, every business-man a blackguard, every lawyer a liar, every policeman a thief, come on Jack, join us, join the racket, royalty demands it, Englands expects, God save the Queen!"'

'Christ!' said Lorrimer, rising to his feet; and a voice in the upper circle demanded, very clearly:

'WHAT ABOUT THE HOLY NAME?'

He heard a little gasp from May Platt, who was on the sofa, and saw her put a handkerchief to her mouth. Coffey stood with one arm in the air, from his previous declaration, but with nothing further coming forth.

Then the ill-experienced youth recovered himself.

'Can't you see it, Father? Listen to me. Just listen. . . .'

Lorrimer was not listening. In the land of saints and scholars an unidentified voice had challenged him on the subject dearest to his heart. He was appalled. He tried to look like a furious business-man while his dazed wits sought the professional opinion of the horribly absent Father Adolphus.

'And when the sun goes down in Shank Lane it's . . . I don't know . . . it's beautiful. Dusk. The air filled with the cries of mothers calling their little bastards in off the street.'

'BLASPHEMY!'

'STOP THE SHOW!'

These were separate shouts from the back of the stalls. May Platt uttered another little cry. Lorrimer was supposed to be moving to the mantelpiece to pick up a figurine, as a weapon, but his feet were cemented to the stage. Fortunately Coffey had now become too lyrical to be halted.

'And at night the music begins. Not that old-fashioned muck you have on records, but music with a beat to it, with a heart to it. Youthful. Youth means something there. It's sad and gay, untouched by your world. It's soft and salty, and innocent. It's . . . it's like fresh butter.'

'DISGUSTING!'

'STOP THE SHOW!'

'Christ!' said Lorrimer very softly, and he strode to the mantelpiece, and the same voice in the upper circle repeated, very loudly:

'WHAT ABOUT THE HOLY NAME?'

Lorrimer held on to the mantelpiece and concentrated desperately on Coffey. Beyond him, on the sofa, May Platt seemed to have swooned away. He was faced with one more exclamation and he was so dazed that he could think of no alternative. Coffey appeared to be strangely determined now.

'I'm going back to Shank Lane, Father!'

'SHAME!'

'AN INSULT TO THE CHURCH!'

'STOP THE SHOW!'

'I'm going back to Honoria! Mother—*you* must come with me!'

'Christ, I'm going to kill you!' said Lorrimer, lifting the figurine from the mantelpiece, raising it above his head, and moving forward.

'WHAT ABOUT THE HOLY NAME?'

'YES, WHAT ABOUT THE HOLY NAME?'

'WHAT ABOUT THE HOLY NAME?'

'WHAT ABOUT THE HOLY NAME?'

His head ringing with this cry, which now came from all parts of the theatre, Lorrimer went for Coffey, clutched at his heart, staggered, fell, stretched himself out, and ultimately lay still.

Coffey bent over him. May Platt should have been there, too, but she was still on the sofa. They should have both sobbed, called for help to take him to the bedroom, and then at last, to the extent that it was decorous under the circumstances, seen the faint indication of a new life together. This they plainly were not going to be able to do, even if May Platt had been capable of standing up, because there was uproar in the auditorium, a shower of litter was raining down on to the stage from the upper circle boxes and a banana skin had landed on top of Lorrimer's prostrate body and had spread its three fingers out across his chest.

Infinitely slowly, the curtain descended.

chapter fifteen

It was intensely exciting in the foyer. The whole of the dress circle and stalls had emerged there, and further movement was impossible. The upper circle had its own side exit, but a great many people had come round to block the front steps. It did not matter, because no one wanted to leave. Everyone was shouting to be heard. It was as if each person sensed deep down that he or she had been present at the outstanding event in the forty or so odd years since the country had won its independence. There were barristers, solicitors, company directors, veterinary surgeons, curtain designers and sales managers of Irish hand-weaving, an internationally famed gynæcologist, Trinity professors, two Church of Ireland clergymen, investigators from the national schools, the youth hostels and the Young Farmers' Association, several Senators, an English-speaking deputy from the Gaelic League and another from the P.E.N. Club, a publicity agent for Waterford glass, a celebrated poet from Guinness's, and the one member of Dail Eireann who was interested in plays and books. Many of them had been outraged by the demonstration, particularly in the dress circle, which was superior to the stalls, thus satisfactorily reversing the social arrangements in London. 'They have disgraced themselves again!' Martin O'Keffe was shouting, with a white face, as he came down the stairs into the packed foyer with Grania. Many others were declaring, with equal passion, that the country had been vilely insulted once more by the purveyors of blasphemous pornography from across the water. The rest were simply enjoying every minute of it.

Among these was Grania, who was eagerly examining every face in the vicinity as they stood in the crush. It had been a glorious Dublin day: they had talked in Dermot's studio while he began his portrait of Hilda, and then gone to order hundreds of invitations for a Christmas party; and now the perfect finale had presented itself. Beside her, Hilda was absorbed too, but in a different way, amounting to total amazement. Grania was certainly most distressed for poor Hugo, but she intended to go and console him and explain to him that in Dublin such experiences must be savoured to the full. Dermot she could not see anywhere. Terence Keogh was close at hand, with his grey mop of hair standing high above the crowd. He was chuckling with unashamed delight. 'The Franciscans were in a box with me,' he shouted at her, 'with the curtains half drawn, because of course it's not allowed, poor dears. Well, they fled! Oh, it was glorious, glorious! I'm going to get roaring drunk.' He seemed to be unaware of the man beside him, who was declaring to sympathetic friends: 'A bloody disgrace, that's what I call it! The Archbishop will have something to say to this—you wait and see!'

Moira was settling her hat. Someone had knocked it into her eyes, and the veil down over her mouth. She was entirely confused. She knew quite well that Tom would have viewed the play as blasphemous and would wish her to go straight home. But there was Ann saying they must go round and apologise for the 'parish pump', whatever she meant by that, and Norah absolutely insisting that they go and comfort Lorrimer. 'Now, Moira, you know as well as I do, he's been abominably treated. I rushed along and left a note at the threatre this evening and it's all settled. We're taking him to Sorrento. Anyhow, Charlie's counting on it. That ought to persuade you.'

'What do you mean by that?' said Moira, holding on to her hat and looking at Norah with alarm. The noise was so great that she could not concentrate.

'He's coming from his Rotary dinner and must be outside now, if only we can get there.'

It was most alarming; and Sorrento was winning a doubtful reputation as Ireland's latest night club, and she was not sure about it at all. The exhibition sherry had given her a headache and her gaiety had departed.

'Ah, come on, Mother,' said Ann. 'We've got to say something. I'll leave the four of you then, and go off home.'

She allowed herself to be pushed towards the steps, where she heard District Justice 'Twitcher' Doyle saying to a laughing group: 'O God, O Manchester'—a witticism that would be retailed for years; and again, as Moira edged past him: 'I wouldn't transport horses like this.' From up on the stairs, only faintly audible here, came the sound of Dermot Sleator singing, with arms outstretched towards the assembly below: 'Oh the English came and tried to teach us their way, and sneered at us for being what we are . . .'

Out on the steps two crones in black shawls were demanding of Moira, in what seemed to be one voice: 'What's goin' on in there, Missus?'

'I don't know, I don't know.'

'Ah God, you might at least tell us!' shouted one of them furiously. 'Bad cess to you, you and your swank hat!'

'How dare you!'

Charlie had suddenly appeared, looking amazingly elegant in his Rotary dinner-suit. Norah was telling him what had happened. 'Christ, that beats everything!' he said. 'Why did I have to miss it?'

She was rather surprised and shocked. She said: 'I think I ought to go home.'

'Now then, now then, what's this!' said Charlie, taking her arm. 'We must visit the unfortunate. He'll soon cheer up at Sorrento. I'm thirsty too.'

Dermot Sleator chested his way out on to the steps, bawling: 'Make way for the author, please!' followed by Grania, Hilda and Martin, and Moira saw them going round towards the stage door.

'All right then,' she said. 'But Tom will never forgive me.'

A moment later, however, as they turned down an alleyway,

she was already excusing herself. Lorrimer was a Catholic. The play was not his fault. He must have been appalled by the things he had to say. Cyril Hampton, the actor who had approved the shape of her bedroom window, had been a Catholic too. A second, turning up so soon, was a stroke of fortune not to be rejected. Tom would understand. Besides, she was on Charlie's arm.

On entering the stage door they found twenty or so people standing in a narrow corridor. It had dark red peeling walls and a stone floor, and was lit by a bare light-bulb. They were waiting to be admitted to Lorrimer's room upstairs, and what was immediately noticeable after the pandemonium outside was that they were absolutely silent like a funeral party. They were obviously expectant and tense about going upstairs. Farthest away, Dermot Sleator and Lawrence Hurley were murmuring together, because Hurley had just reported the sale of ten pictures. Mrs Hurley was there too: rather dumpy and unattractive Moira thought, compared with her slender, distinguished husband. She could not imagine by what right Grania Agerton-Willy and her offensively Protestant-sounding woman friend were about to introduce themselves to Lorrimer. Also present were two Dublin drama critics. They were whispering jokes to each other, and appeared to be in a state of delight, in shameless contrast to everyone else. She recognised them because both had been in Cyril Hampton's dressing-room, drinking his whisky.

Because he was standing beside her, she noted the heavy presence of 'Teeth' Murphy. His wife was with him. She was also invariably agreeable, and her personality was even less apparent than her husband's. 'Teeth' was, for once, not smiling. He murmured solemnly to Moira: 'I feel it's up to all of us to make some sort of amends, don't you?'

'I do indeed,' said Norah.

Both she and Moira were conscious that Agerton-Willy was ignoring them. Ann looked at her closely, remembering that her son had come to tea. She had been remembering it all evening, until chaos had intervened.

Martin O'Keeffe said abruptly: 'Of course it was a naïve work, but by God it had its lesson for the gombeen-men, and they damn well recognised it.'

'Do you really think they're capable of that?' said Ann. 'I'm sure they thought it was about Manchester magnates only.'

'It didn't require much perception,' said Martin, looking at her with interest. 'They know their own.'

'I assumed their reaction to be more simple than that.'

'Of course it was, Martin!' said Grania, also glancing approvingly at Ann.

'Good evening,' said Moira.

'Oh, good evening.'

'You've met Mrs Gerraty?'

'Ah, you were talking about her earlier, weren't you? How do you do?'

'And Mr Gerraty?'

'How do you do?'

'Very pleased to meet you,' said Charlie. 'I've hoped for that pleasure for some time.'

'Really?'

He smiled, knowing that Father Hanna must already have used his powers of persuasion, and they were now at least commercially related; and Moira felt a stab of jealousy, fearing for an instant that he was going to kiss her hand.

'Ah!' said Grania, because a boy was on the stairs saying they could all come up now.

They climbed the stairs and went along a narrow corridor in Indian file, with Grania's scarlet baneen suit showing the way like a beacon in front. They heard shouting from the dressing-rooms, and Jeremy Coffey came out of one of them, slammed the door, crossed the corridor into another, and slammed that door too. Another door was open, and through it they saw May Platt stretched out on a couch surrounded by Nigerians and two St John Ambulance men who were bent over her, fanning her with a white towel.

Grania followed the boy into Lorrimer's room and Norah, who was behind her, suddenly stood rigidly in the doorway, causing collisions and exclamations all the way down the line.

'What is it?' said Moira, her view entirely obstructed by Norah's tall form, in its silky green dress.

Norah could not speak.

Grania's neat figure was enfolded in Lorrimer's arms. She had heard them both say: 'Darling.'

'Will you get on with it up front!' roared Dermot, from somewhere down the corridor. 'The rest of us have our need as well.'

Norah had been thinking quickly and cursed Charlie. She had privately ascertained at once on his arrival outside that he had not even troubled to telephone Father Hanna, being so engaged on his damn dinner. This would have been the moment to explode the bombshell. As it was, she stepped into the room and had to hear Grania say: 'Darling, it was too frightful for you. They're such boors. One can only regard it as a madhouse and feel pity for them.'

'I take exception to that,' said Norah, as the others moved in behind her. 'You'll find the real Irish people are not so boorish, Mr Lorrimer. I'm Norah Gerraty, you'll have had my note?'

'Oh yes . . . yes,' said Lorrimer. This was all a nightmare. Shortly he would wake up.

'My wife is a little over-excited,' began Charlie.

'Evidently,' said Grania. 'Hugo, darling, you don't know Hilda Manningham and Martin O'Keeffe.' She looked around for Dermot, and saw that he had lagged behind in the doorway and was opening a bottle of whisky with one of the drama critics.

So did Lorrimer. 'Do, please, all have a drink,' he said. He was paler than he had made-up for Act Three. A furious set-to had taken place with the theatre manager; Lorrimer maintaining that he was responsible for the audience and the manager alleging that he had been grossly deceived by the play, having been absent throughout rehearsals as one of the three judges in the Tipperary section of a nation-wide beauty queen contest.

The other drama critic opened the other bottle, and everyone was talking happily again.

'Teeth' Murphy came up to Lorrimer and made a speech of which he comprehended very little.

Martin told him that the play was a challenge, to which he replied 'Oh', and 'Thank you very much.'

Ann shook his hand and said that they all owed him an apology.

Moira recalled having seen him in the film *Witty But Nice,* which she described as gorgeous.

Terence Keogh appeared, holding a tumbler of dark whisky, and asked him about Father Adolphus, whom he described as 'a dear sweet priest'.

Norah Gerraty interrupted with the words: 'We hear he's quite wonderful,' and told him that her two sons were at Downside and she hoped that one of them, named Vernon, would complete his education in France.

Dermot strode forward, handed him a large neat whisky, and said: 'You'll need this. Pay no attention, you poor foreigner. It's all the fault of James Conolly.'

'Oh, who?' inquired Lorrimer. But a young man took him by the arm and pulled him decisively aside.

'I'm phoning a story to Fleet Street. What did you think of it all, eh, Mr Lorrimer?'

'What do you imagine I thought?' said Lorrimer, suddenly beginning to regain a little colour.

'You'll leave it to my imagination, sir?'

'I shouldn't have thought it needed very much.'

'Thank you. That's all I wanted. Sorry, for barging in like this.'

Lawrence Hurley had approached, and he looked quite civilised; almost English.

'All my sympathy, Mr Lorrimer,' he said. 'I run a gallery here, and I've suffered similarly in my time. In my case, from the Church, I'm afraid. Strictly between you and me.'

'I beg your pardon?'

'Not, I'm afraid, appreciative of the arts.'

'*Not,* you say?'

'Oh. Well, perhaps in England, Mr Lorrimer, perhaps in England.'

The Fleet Street representative had sought out Grania, who was not hostile. On the contrary, some of the reports of her Horse Show dance had excelled even the event itself. Yes, she was holding a dance shortly before Christmas, and an airline friend would as usual provide a plane for guests from across the water. This time they would want particularly to get back to their children, and so on.

'You gentlemen will all be asked as usual, of course,' she said.

Moira, being small, had been pushed towards the doorway, among a group of people she scarcely knew at all. They seemed to be lawyers and their wives. Because Moira was uninvolved, 'Teeth' Murphy's wife, whose conversation was like lead, had moved closer, and so had the dumpy Mrs Hurley, who was equally uninspiring. In fact she had recalled, with quiet alarm, that she had been at Loreto Convent school with Mrs Hurley, whom Norah Gerraty—or Fitzgibbon, as she then was—a senior girl, had unkindly named 'suet pudding'. Norah, she noted, now had Lorrimer's ear. She had been reminded of Loreto by the way Norah stormed in upon Lorrimer and Agerton-Willy. That was exactly how she had been as a senior girl. It had obviously disturbed Charlie, for some reason, which was no harm. He was close at hand, telling some kind of funny story to one of the critics, and she felt daring and desperate enough to raise her voice.

'Is Mr Lorrimer coming with us?'

He finished his story and the critic roared with laughter. It looked as if it might have been improper somehow. He turned and said: 'You bet your life! The wife has taken charge, as ever. We'll have to wait till the crowd clears. Won't be long. This whisky's almost gone.'

'We'd better be off, Tim,' said the critic. 'Blessings on the un-expected curtain, but time's running out. They'll be going to bed. Read us in the morning!' he added to Charlie, with a grin.

'They've a nerve,' said Moira.

'Damned on your own whisky,' said Charlie. 'An unhappy fate.'

It almost seemed as if he was amused.

'It'd make you feel ashamed.'

'I like your fire,' he said.

'It's nothing to Norah's when she gets going.'

'Ah, that's a little too much.'

'Ah, go on. You're well able for it.'

'Me? I'm the mildest of husbands. May I come with you to Sorrento? Norah will drive the great man.'

'All right.'

'What about your beautiful daughter?'

'She's gone. She went home. She likes to be independent, God help her. I don't know what to do about it. Why, was it *she* you wanted to drive with?' she inquired, astonished by the sudden possibility.

'Not at all. Not at all, my dear Moira. It was you.'

They were leaving now, Moira noted: the Murphys and Hurleys and several strangers. Dermot Sleator said there had not been enough to sing on, and owing to Act Three being abbreviated, the pubs were still open. Agerton-Willy asked Lorrimer to go with them, but he said: 'Another time, darling. Mrs Gerraty has very kindly invited me to her club.' She looked very put out, and left with her party.

At last they were alone.

'Moira and I are eloping together,' said Charlie. 'Will you take Mr Lorrimer in my car?'

'With pleasure,' said Norah.

Lorrimer put on a black overcoat with an alpaca collar. The whisky and the increasingly cheerful company had achieved what he would have conceived an impossibility. There was evidently nothing final in lying on a stage under a shower of banana-skins. He would have assumed it to be professional ruin, possibly giving cause for suicide, and thus mortal sin. But that must be in other countries. These people appeared to have forgotten about it already, and he was very nearly in the same condition. The wine of the country produced what he would have termed a delicious glow.

All was now quiet in the corridors. But outside in the street two thin, middle-aged men in mackintoshes were already picketing the theatre. They walked up and down holding posters on which someone had scrawled, obviously in haste: 'Boycott This Play' and 'An Insult to the Church'. Black lettering at the bottom of the posters announced that they were representatives of the Confraternity of the Happy Death.

A few men in a pub doorway and a distant, watchful policeman were the only remaining spectators.

Lorrimer felt the glow rapidly leaving him.

'Who are they?' he murmured. 'What is this?'

'Don't worry your head about that,' said Norah. She was struggling with a green coat which Charlie had remembered to hand her, brusquely, as he disappeared. Lorrimer helped her, graciously, on with it.

'But it's a Confraternity,' he said.

'Don't worry about it, my dear,' said Norah, taking his arm and leading him across the road. 'They should have more sense.' She wondered how much Agerton-Willy had meant by 'darling', and he as well. He was a gentleman, and she had not met one for years. His appearance was striking too.

They got into Charlie's Borgward, and he sat regally beside her.

Evidently in the year and more since Paul Casey had left for the agricultural college at Cirencester she had not lost her well-known effect on men. It was only now clearly apparent to her that she had very rapidly taken control of one of the leading English actors of stage and screen, and a total stranger. She had, however, vaguely wondered all the time if he was married, and nearly taken the opportunity to find out when she was speaking to him about Vernon. But it was perhaps better not to know. She released the clutch and drove off with a flourish, ignoring the parking attendant who was approaching the window for money.

Moira and Charlie were very close together in her baby car. He put his arm along the seat behind her and she could feel his hand touching her back. She was terrified about driving. At first she could not find the key in her handbag. Then she could not find the knob for the lights. When you lived in the mountains, opportunities for driving at night were rare; and she was usually in Tom's Jaguar. When she was ready the wretched attendant came to the window, and she began to look in her handbag again, but Charlie leaned across her and gave her a half-crown, no less. This had placed her almost in an embrace and her heart was pattering. She put the gear into first, released the clutch, and went suddenly backwards very fast, bumping into and nearly killing one of the men from the Confraternity of the Happy Death. He shouted, and she could see him in the mirror gesticulating with his poster.

'Ah, shut your bawling,' said the attendant. 'Drive on, ma'am. Pay no attention. Don't mind him. Except you're in reverse.'

She fought with the gear lever.

Charlie roared with laughter. It was not as refined as she would have expected. It was like an explosion, and it made her jump.

'God, I'm terribly sorry,' she said. 'I don't know what happened.'

They went forward in jerks.

'Oh, that was lovely, lovely!' he said, still laughing. 'Wait till we tell old Lorrimer. You struck a blow there, all right!'

His hand went up to her shoulder. Of all hopeless situations at such a moment, she thought, to be driving a car! Very slowly she guided it down the centre of the street. The lights were still on in the new arcade that had been made for the tourists in Irish contemporary style, with 'boutiques' displaying tweed, rugs, woollen ties, glassware, pottery by native artists, and genuine Aran Island sweaters, with snake-like patterns, lots of little blobs, and every intricacy of the knitter's art. People were coming out of a darkened cinema that had been showing a reissue of *My Man Godfrey*.

'Aren't you frozen,' she said, 'without an overcoat? I don't have a heater, I'm afraid.'

He put his hand on the back of her fur collar.

'I don't need one,' he said.

She had to glance at his lined, handsome face and his thick, wavy black hair, and very nearly was foolish enough to remark that his suit was smart. He must be strong and healthy. Tom was hardly ever without his new camel-hair overcoat which she thought flashy, but he said it was necessary for property development. It showed confidence in the houses.

Charlie felt it to be an entirely safe situation, because when the Neelans heard the news there was not likely to be any further intimacy. He also found her an attractive little thing, if over-talkative.

He had been having a most agreeable evening with the Rotary boys, and particularly with some cattle-dealer friends he had met in the hotel bar after the dinner was over. This theatre world was a woman's world, and he felt ill-at-ease in it, although it was his gift to appear to be at ease wherever he was. He had never in his life been in a dressing-room before, and considered that there was something odd, and totally outside his sphere, about gentlemen who made up their faces there. His wife's animosity towards Agerton-Willy, strictly contrary to his advice, had not improved the experience, although Father Hanna had presumably advanced matters sufficiently for it to be of small importance now. He was extremely confident that the Major would prefer a proposition from such an eminent quarter, which would preserve his former property, in contrast to the alternative: wholesale destruction by a speculator on the make. The only obstacles had been the need to investigate the price and Neelan's readiness to pay it, and in this Father Hanna had been more adept than himself. However, he had not been all that interested, and was not even concerned to discover the outcome now. Commissions like this one from the Fathers were coming in all the time.

'I wonder were they right to stop the show?' said Moira. 'Of course Norah and Ann wouldn't even consider it. But I wouldn't be surprised if Tom thought them right.'

For some absurd reason she not only felt the compulsion to re-call Tom's existence, but was even dying to tell him that Tom was going up for Senator. With part of her dream almost coming true, it seemed perverse and mad, and she added quickly:

'Personally I'm sick of these English people who think they can tell us off, with their rock 'n' roll and all the rest of it!'

'I *said* I liked your fire.'

'Bringing their dirty notions to a clean-living, Christian coun-try! Of course I don't include Mr Lorrimer, who seems quite a different type.'

He was not Charlie's type. He was a ladies' man. It was a cause superficially for pleasure, and ultimately and profoundly, for an-noyance, that the ladies regarded himself in the same light; alarm-ingly so in the case of the French girl at Cannes, where he had been much more interested in the casino. In Dublin his interests were drinking, racing, yachting and squash. The elder boy, An-drew, who was nearly eighteen, was very good at squash. They played at Fitzwilliam in the holidays. Vernon did not. Fortunately in Dublin he was permitted, most of the time, to enjoy these pleasures. But they did ask to be flirted with, and he did enjoy it when it went no further. In this case the situation was ideal. In-deed he wondered just how outraged the Neelans were going to be when they heard the news. He had only let Norah in on the secret that morning, and even she was angry enough: accusing him of wickedly deceiving a friend with whom she was inno-cently going to the theatre that very night. Of course her indig-nation was tempered by the knowledge that Grania Agerton-Willy was due for a shock, but then she also had an inexplicable affection for the Major. These human and social complexities—

always a bore and a feminine delight—would soon be removed. But the present moment was to be enjoyed, and that was another of his talents.

They were crossing the river. The tide was in and he saw the swans drifting on the black water.

'I'm very happy that Fate has brought us together,' he said. 'Norah used to speak of her old school friend, and I have admired from afar. But I never imagined we would meet.'

'Ah, go on with you,' she said, very nearly swerving into a cyclist with no lights. 'D'you remember the Contemporary Tweed Dance?'

'The what?'

'It was before you went to Cannes. We met there.'

'Good God, of course we did. But rather formally, if I remember. That's not what I mean.'

After a moment she said: 'How *did* Fate bring us together, by the way? You phoned Tom. I often wondered why. I believe you still haven't seen him.'

'No, no. The occasion passed. Someone else took over.'

'You're *most* mysterious. Was it to do with houses?'

She was strongly tempted to reveal her own secret: Tom's plan for Edenmore. She had also been tempted in the dressing-room, when Norah was at odds with Agerton-Willy. It would have given Norah some glorious ammunition.

'No, no. Tom sticks to his own designer—or builder, should I say?'

'You sound disapproving.'

'Not at all. That would be against professional etiquette.'

'In any case, you'd be far too expensive. Everyone knows that.'

'Ha, ha! For the bold Tom? I doubt it very much.'

He was on the point of saying that Norah had told him Tom was to go up for Senator, and having a little fun out of it. But she would remember afterwards, and it would add to the bitterness.

They were moving very slowly along the Strand Road, because she could not remember where Norah had said Sorrento was.

'Tell me about your work,' she said. 'It must be exciting.'

'Ah, this is no time for that.'

He scarcely ever spoke of it. That, too, had been exemplified at Cannes, where his friends David Keeley, James Larkin and Kevin Barry were all architects. David worked under him in Stephen's Green, and the other two were in another firm. But it was for their leisure-time bachelor pleasures that he enjoyed their company, and he had refused to talk 'shop.' He was almost the only architect in the country who knew a damn thing about Jolainin and Frank Lloyd Wright, and when not at work he enjoyed all the discussion he wanted by reading architectural journals from abroad. By contrast with these friends, the Brophys fighting with each other, the Callinans boring each other, and his own curiously distant relationship, showed what happened when women were allowed to make a serious entry on the scene.

'Ah, I've spotted it!' said Moira. It was a small red neon sign, 'Sorrento', down a side street, above a door at the bottom of an area steps.

The Borgward was parked outside.

Norah had made what she felt to be a considerable advance in understanding. Driving away from the theatre she had breathed deeply with relief. Even escaping momentarily from Moira, after Charlie's inexcusable revelation, was a comfort. Bitterly, she wished that he had kept his information for another day. But he had done it deliberately, of course.

There had been other dangers in the theatre. The Callinans had been seated two rows ahead. If they had been wearisome at Cannes they had been deadly bores at the dance in the Gresham on Saturday. Beside them sat the gynæcologist who had produced both boys, which for some reason she always found slightly embarrassing. It only wanted the battling Brophys to make the evening complete. That was the peril of Dublin. It was why she had stayed away from the Baldoyle races, even though it had meant an interminable afternoon at Finlandia. In consequence, she had not been able to concentrate overmuch on the play. As she had hoped, it spoke certainly for abandonment of all restraint, but from the point of view of the young only, and against Lorrimer, whom she *had* watched with great attention.

'I've lost my black hat,' he said, as they drove away. 'I must have left it in my room. It was all rather exciting.'

'Will I turn back?'

'No, no. I wouldn't dream of it.'

'Are you sure?'

'Quite sure. It's unimportant.'

'It sounds very distinguished,' she said. 'It must suit you.' She glanced at him. He was certainly rather bald. But his nose and chin were most impressive.

He had fully meant that it was unimportant. He was feeling extraordinarily well. His little party had been a rousing success. He had forgotten that it was the management that had produced the whisky for the drama critics, and like the others he was unaware that Terence Keogh was at that moment lying unconscious behind the screen placed there for actresses entertaining admirers.

'My wife would have enjoyed tonight,' he said.

'Enjoyed it? Your wife?'

'Yes. She's a novelist. She writes risqué novels under the name of Veronica Blake.'

'Oh. I haven't heard of her. But I expect they're banned here.'

'Banned?'

'Yes. Vernon would know. He's the reader in the family.'

Lorrimer was laughing; which meant a rumbling noise and a heaving of his considerable front.

'I find that delightful. Veronica banned. These somewhat narrow attitudes have their charms, after all. Well, well. Oh dear, oh dear.'

'You sound quite pleased.'

'Oh, it wouldn't worry her. I hope they ban her next one!'

'What a thing to say! I thought it was only Irishmen who spoke of their wives like that.'

'You don't know the circumstances, my dear. I think it must be your delightful whisky that tempts me to indiscretion, but I'll tell you. I myself am grossly represented—or misrepresented—in the same work.'

'You are? Well, I never! How could she do a thing like that?'

'Oh, she could. She could.'

'Good Lord! Tch, tch!'

'It's due in about ten days' time, so that if *The Kiss of Death* continues after tonight I shall still be here. Certainly after your demonstration of support tonight *I* have every intention of continuing, but the management seems disturbed.'

'Oh, of course it'll go on.'

'So my new-found enemies may read about me.'

'Oh, no one reads here! There'd be no question of that. In any case, if her books have been banned before, they'll hold this one for inspection till about next spring, banned or no. Vernon's given me a lecture on all that. He gets very hot under the collar about it.'

'I see. At least I think I see. I must say I'm beginning to find everything here absolutely fascinating.'

'Really? You're most forgiving, Mr Lorrimer. We don't deserve it.'

'Hugo is my name, my dear.'

'Hugo. It's very distinguished. Mine's Norah. It's rather common, isn't it? I wish I agreed with you about it being fascinating. I want to live abroad. France. I'd love to live in France.'

'How interesting, Norah. I like Norah very much: Irish and charming. But you're not happy here? With a handsome husband, and a son . . . ?'

'Two sons.'

'Two, is it? And living in this beautiful city? Look at this river. It's like the Seine. Your life sounds complete to me.'

'Perhaps that's what's wrong.'

'You are an interesting woman.'

'Am I?'

'Indeed you are.'

They crossed the river and drove along the Strand Road. 'Where are you stealing me away to, Norah?' asked Hugo.

'We're almost there. It's our night club. A *petite boîte*. It's only been open a week, and I don't know it, but Charlie had a wild night there with some of the boys. They've got some dodge for serving drink after hours. Charlie knows the ropes.'

'There's *not* likely to be a floor show, I take it?'

It was his voice, she suddenly realised. That was his greatest attraction: an actor's, cultivated, English voice, compared with Charlie's Dublin accent.

'Heavens, no. But I believe a man plays the piano.'

'I'd always connected a certain freedom with Catholic countries, compared with my Calvinist land. But this is all a most intriguing surprise.'

'*I'm* more intrigued by the French customs.'

'Really?'

She drew up outside the sign 'Sorrento' and turned and saw him smiling quizzically at her. She smiled too, and laughed, and said: 'Come along now.'

They went down the stairs through the door and pushed aside a heavy red curtain. A waiter took their coats. For a mad moment Norah thought that he was the escaped English convict whose photograph she had seen in the *Daily Express*. But this man had no moustache. Inside it was dark. Little red lights illuminated about fifteen tables with red check cloths. There was a small bar at one end, a small dance-floor at the centre, and a man with a scarred face, in a dark suit, playing 'Just One of Those Things' on the piano at the other end. About twenty people were scattered about the room in the semi-darkness.

The Callinans were seated at the table nearest the pianist.

Fortunately they were with two people unknown to Norah, and she led the way to the table nearest the bar, conscious that her arrival with Lorrimer was leaving them dumbstruck.

She and Hugo sat with their backs to a wallpaper showing white yachts sailing on a blue sea. The proprietor had not been in the country long enough to learn about Irish 'contemporary', and so had hit upon the gaiety of Sorrento, having picked up rolls of this paper cheap in Holland. It did not, in fact, represent Sorrento at all, but the Dutch seaside resort of Scheveningen. However, sea and yachts did not vary much. His name was Stavros Caramanos. He was a Neapolitan of Greek descent who had suddenly moved over from Amsterdam. His *petite boîte,* consisting of one large room and a small kitchen, and now looking rather different, had recently been occupied by a labourer, his wife and five children, but the council had finally moved them out to a villa in the suburbs.

The arrival of Caramanos had introduced many newspaper readers to a new word, 'Interpol', but no one was clear what it was all about, and people who were familiar with London, the South of France and so on, were only too eager to give their patronage to a night spot in Dublin at last. Whatever the trouble was, it had prevented him from being granted anything better than a public house license, but he had so far circumvented this. In order to keep the neighbouring slum-dwellers from his door he insisted on the consumption of food at prices comparable to those in the better Dublin restaurants; as, for example, bacon and eggs at seven and sixpence, and a mixed grill at fifteen shillings.

Caramanos was in fact, present, at one of the tables, smoking cigars with three friends, Hans Schneider, a Swiss-German stamp dealer, Arthur Pomfret, a British publisher of nature magazines, and Francesco Pastorelli, a salesman of second-hand cars who had flown over unexpectedly from London that afternoon under the name of Cyril Smith. To his horror and total bewilderment, he had been surrounded by reporters at the airport and vigorously questioned about Beethoven's Fourth Piano Concerto and the acoustics of the Theatre Royal, and had quickly said that he approved both, since privately he was hoping to set up a small business here. However, Caramanos had assured him that this was all to the good: indeed, since no photographs had been taken, it was heaven-sent.

Hugo was very satisfied. He thought the place delightfully quaint and Irish, compared with the oppressive luxuriousness of the London equivalents. He rather wished that the other two were not coming. This tall, bronzed woman was beginning to have an effect on him.

Norah was proud of her 'find', and forgot that it was Charlie's.

The others arrived. Moira was curiously excited. She had surrendered her hat and coat. 'Isn't it attractive, Norah!' she whispered breathlessly as she joined them at the tables. 'How clever of him! This is just the sort of place Tom would like to open.'

'Would he approve it?' said Norah.

'Oh, he's very broad-minded, you know. On certain matters.'

They ordered bacon and eggs, and the waiter brought them whiskies all round, and Charlie paid. He had noted the Callinans, and had also avoided them.

Hugo looked contentedly about him, placed his hands, folded together, on the table—one of them displaying a large ring—and as if he had suddenly thought of it, said:

'By the way, Norah, I was confused by your somewhat dramatic entry after the show. I could not quite follow your point, nor why my dear friend, Grania, took it amiss. You made some reference to "the real Irish".'

'Well you see, she's not Irish, Hugo, and she knows it.'

Moira was astonished by the Christian names.

'Not Irish?' Hugo exclaimed. 'Grania? Not Irish?'

'Not a bit of it,' said Norah.

'She's British,' Moira explained. 'She's a Protestant.'

'Or West British if you like,' Norah added.

'But in London I've always taken Grania to be the epitome of Irishness, in the most delightful way.'

'Well, she's taken you in, I'm afraid,' said Norah. 'We're the real Irish.'

'My goodness me,' said Hugo. 'She's taken us all in, in that case. All her London friends.'

'You're an old friend, are you?'

'Oh, rather. I've known Grania for I suppose about thirty years.'

Norah recalled that she had ill-advisedly asked the Major to tell Grania about her party. Perhaps she would not come. One thing was certain: the Neelans were unlikely to be there.

'Shall we dance?' said Charlie to Moira. The conversation was coming too close to current events.

'I'd love to.'

They joined several couples who were now on the floor. The pianist never paused. He was playing 'These Foolish Things'. Moira sang softly: 'The winds of March that made my heart a dancer.'

He danced beautifully, unlike all other Irishmen, including Tom who did an awful kind of a jig and nothing else.

'How could *you* know anyone for thirty years?' Norah inquired, turning her penetrating eyes on Hugo. 'Sure you're only a slip of a lad.'

'Ha, ha, now I do recognise the real Irish. The blarney, eh?'

'Not at all.'

She saw the Callinans preparing an approach.

'Let's dance,' she said.

'With pleasure, my dear.'

'You came, you saw, you conquered me,' the pianist was playing.

He danced beautifully, unlike all Irishmen, except possibly Charlie.

'By the way,' she said, 'we're having a house-warming on Sunday week. I chose Sunday especially for you.'

'How charming of you. Really, my dear, I've never had such hospitality. I'm afraid it would not happen in England.'

'I expect you're accustomed to dancing with lovely young actresses?'

'Oh, ho, don't you believe it! You don't know Veronica.'

'I often wished I'd had the chance of young people nowadays. Going to London and so on. I spent my youth in a wretched job here, with little company worth speaking of.'

'Perhaps you've made up for it since, my dear.'

'Oh, I'm afraid not.'

'I find it hard to believe that.'

The others were soon moving back to the table. Charlie became bored by dancing very quickly, and he liked drinking.

'I was remembering the hops in the tennis club in the old days,' said Moira. 'They'd a wonderful pianist. We had great times. I was secretary to the manager of the Munster and Leinster bank, you know. Lots of free time and plenty of company.'

The waiter came and murmured in Charlie's ear that the bar was closed.

'We'll have the usual with our food,' said Charlie.

'You must have less company out in the mountains now,' he said.

He had placed his hand on hers and she was not able to speak for a moment.

'Oh, it's awful, Charlie. Honest to God, I don't see a soul.'

'Dear me. I don't know those parts very well. You must be above Cullen's. I've had a few wild nights out there with some of the lads.'

'You don't say! I heard it was a dreadful place. Tom wouldn't hear of going there.'

'What lads?' she wondered. He was not so young.

'Oh, it's not as wicked as all that.'

'There's another one nearer us: O'Sullivan's. The light blazing away half the night, and singing and God knows what. Tom's very put out that the new law didn't stop all that.'

The bacon and eggs, cups, saucers and a large white teapot with a cracked spout, were placed on the table; and Hugo and Norah returned. They had been dancing in an intimate manner. Whose idea it was, he was not sure, but he now felt exhilarated.

'Splendid!' he said, examining the repast as he sat down. 'May I make a speech?'

'A what?' said Moira.

'Do, Hugo, do,' said Norah.

'Well, you know, as an Englishman, with half the world seemingly turning against us these days, I'm ready to confess that you've done really splendid things here. It's a foreign land. You have developed your own attitudes, your own culture, your own way of looking at things. And I'm in a good position to say it—ha, ha! No, all joking apart, one can see now the complete justification for your historic fight for self-government.'

'Hurray!' said Moira, beginning to like him at last.

Charlie was pouring from the teapot.

'Ah, it's good and strong too!' said Hugo. 'But it looks cold?'

'You bet your life,' said Charlie. 'You don't like your whisky hot, do you?'

part three

It was Sunday week, and raining at last: the soft, mysterious Irish rain. Tom Neelan stood at the drawing-room window, with one gingery eyebrow lowered to protect his eye from the smoke rising from the cigarette beneath his ginger moustache. He looked with satisfaction, and even a pleasing sense of dominance, upon the vista. Away across County Meath and the great Central Plain, the country was at the bottom of a tank. A vast black lid of cloud had been placed over it. Dublin had totally disappeared. A little of the Bay was still visible, looking grey and desolate, but the peninsula of Howth had also gone. The nearer landscape remained, however: his red houses with grey slate roofs and, better still, the Murrough-Bryants in the trees below.

In his wallet he carried a letter from the Major, asking him to meet at the estate agents in the morning, to effect a sale.

Moira was sitting by the fire, over the remains of tea, reading a pile of newspapers. She was checking up on Lorrimer's position, preparatory to metting him again at the Finlandia house-warming. Each of the Irish Sunday newspapers had an article by a leading cleric on the immoral implications of *The Kiss of Death,* which was now playing to packed houses. Indeed, there had been clashes in the street outside between ticket touts, who were doing furious business, and members of the Confraternity of the Happy Death. For ten days there had been events sufficiently momentous to drive all other news out of the headlines. On the second night the police had removed several members of the theatre management to Mountjoy prison. But their release had followed next day on the condition that references to the Holy Name were in every case to be amended to the words 'By Gum', which Lorrimer was now uttering with relish and relief. Meanwhile the

Irish Times correspondence column had come into its own yet again, and Moira Neelan had been buying and reading what she conceived to be this West British newspaper for the first time in her life; with no sense of guilt, because the longest letters of all, in opposition to the performance, were coming from a Catholic ecclesiastic of high position. Others came from Sneem and Ballinascorthy, from writers clearly of the opposite persuasion, who discussed the essence of morality as conceived by Soren Kierkegaard and Benedetto Croce, while confessing that they had not been able to get up to Dublin to see the play. The same was true of the ecclesiastic, who lived in Limerick. The whole correspondence was eventually to be published in book form, selling at one shilling, and entitled *Morality and the Kiss of Death*. But as yet it was still running fiercely.

Moira had read some extracts out loud, but had given up doing so in irritation, because Tom, who had not seen the play, was treating the crisis very light-heartedly. She would have been astonished, had she not known that it was all on account of his triumph over Edenmore. He was much too pleased with himself. He had not even been interested in the English newspaper which quoted—invented, in Moira's opinion—a furious denunciation made by Lorrimer in his dressing-room, ' "You can easily imagine my feelings," Lorrimer told me. "In thirty years of acting life I have never before been treated to such a display of vulgar hooliganism, masquerading to the point of blasphemy, as religious protest. This city is a provincial sink." '

'*Panem et circenses,*' said Tom, which like so much of his conversation held no meaning for her. 'By tomorrow we shall doubtless have had some new local *scandale,* and it will all be forgotten.'

This had put her in mind of something else, which had been simmering ever since the bewildering scenes at Mass that morning.

She now broke the silence, and taking off her spectacles and holding them in her lap said, aggressively to cover her nervousness, because he might well throw a fit: 'There's something else that may interest you more. I haven't bothered you because you were so busy, but it's as much your responsibility as mine.'

'Speak, my dear. We shall bear the yoke between us.'

'Oh, you're very facetious today! Well, listen to this. I ran into Brendan when I was in town on Wednesday. We had a cup of coffee, and he told me, pretending to pass it off, you know what I mean, that he drove round to Ann's after work the evening we were going to the theatre . . . and do you know who she was saying good-bye to on the steps, cool as a cucumber, in full view of anyone that happened to be passing?'

'I cannot imagine.'

'Patrick Price-Jones—from down below!'

'*Tiens, tiens.*'

'Never mind the French.'

'This is good news.'

'It's *what?*'

'A well-educated fellow. *Bien élevé,* as they say. This connection must be fostered; for the time being, at any rate. It may easily have been the direct cause of his grandfather's deciding to entrust me with his property.'

'Property, property! Business! Sometimes I wonder, Tom Neelan, if you're not going out of your senses. "Fostered," you say. Are you aware that he's a Protestant? An English settler with a foreign name! Good for nothing . . . out of work . . . and with no religion whatever. Are you so steeped in your wretched business that you're prepared to trade in your own daughter to a pagan with no morals?'

'Now, now. Now, now. That is scarcely in question. Between the *via media,* and the ultimate there are many gradations.'

'I don't know what that means, but *we* were married, if you remember, after a few weeks.'

'There were no impediments . . . impedimenta.'

'And I know all about English people and their gradations, thank you very much. You should have seen that play! Yes, you should! There'll be no gradations for *my* daughter, I can tell you that, Tom Neelan.'

'Come, come. Let us say no more. You are over-excited.'

She gazed at the papers on the sofa beside her, shocked, amazed, and unable to see anything except a blur.

She had been preparing her announcement ever since Mass when they had all been subjected to an alarming experience. Father Hanna had unleashed a quite extraordinary invective on the subject of two unnamed persons who were up to something unspecified in the area and proposed to complete the business in England. There had been peculiar gasps from Kathleen, who always sat with her sister, Finola, and Julia Byrne, discreetly removed from Tom and herself, in the back pew of the church. Then the odd-looking son of the Murrough-Bryants' gardener, being present on one of his rare visits, had risen, left his father, and walked straight out down the aisle, leading Paddy, the farm boy, behind him. She had no idea what was going on, and was not attending very closely because, as Father Hanna's voice continued to shake the foundations of the building, she had been stricken with the appalling notion that he was talking about Ann and Patrick Price-Jones. But after a moment of cold fear she had realised that the idea was absurd. It was, however, a future possibility, and if there was any question of a liaison it must be exploded immediately.

The fact that they might well be meeting without hindrance contrasted very sharply in her mind with her own predicament. For the past ten days no valid cause had presented itself for seeing Charlie again. Fate, having introduced them, had exhibited its traditional cruelty by taking no further interest.

But he would be at Finlandia.

So would Ann.

'Now just you listen to me for a minute,' she said. 'Brendan is bringing her to the party. D'you know what you're going to do? You're going to take him aside and have a few serious words with him.'

'Oh my dear, it's not really the time nor the place, and I don't fancy myself as an *advocatus diaboli.*'

'Whatever that may be, I couldn't care less! It's time this was brought to a head. He's like all Irishmen. He's got to be driven to it. And you're going to do it. Today! Now, ring for Kathleen and she'll clear the tea-things away. I'm going upstairs to get ready.'

As she went out, he pressed the bell by the fireplace, saying: 'Dear me. Dear me.'

It was growing dark outside: no longer the darkness of the Celtic twilight, but common-or-garden night. He turned on the standard-lamp, sat down, took up his book, and read:

'Crushed Youngsters.'

He smiled.

'In the early period nearly half the losses may be put down to mothers crushing their youngsters. This may quite easily happen by day as well as during the night. The mother first lies across the youngsters, partially suffocating them, and then, when they are unable to move, she crushes them by changing her position.'

It was Dr Heinrich Stumpff on the Pig Industry.

Kathleen entered, in such a state of excitement that when she lifted the tray everything rattled and clattered and the milk spilt over the remains of the food. She hurried out, conscious that the Master was watching her in a surprised way. Her appointment at the priest's house was at six, and the time was drawing near. She went into the servants' bathroom, where the tea-things were usually washed up, allowing Julia Byrne free play in the kitchen for cooking the dinner. She deposited the tray, studied with satisfaction the arrangement of sheets and garments on the drying-stand, which so perfectly hid the bath, and leaning over the top of it inquired: 'Are you all right?'

'Oh, yes, Kathleen. I'm grand.'

A use had at last been found for the bath. Her younger sister, Deirdre, was stretched out in it among blankets and pillows, with Richard, the collie, lying on top of her. She was reading the paperback edition of *The Song of Bernadette*. She had been in residence here, undetected by the Neelans, for three days and nights. The only real risk was that she ate almost twice as much as Kathleen and Julia Byrne together, and the Mistress might wonder where the food was going.

Deirdre was the sister who had previously been regarded as a bit soft in the head. She must now be cured because she had decided to become a nun. Kathleen had been impressed and Julia Byrne almost in transports under her cold exterior. Lacking the courage to declare her intention at home, Deirdre had arrived at midnight in a state of distress. Even normally she had a white face with large rolling eyes, and was striking, in a way different to Finola.

'I'm going to Father Hanna now,' said Kathleen. 'He won't be long settling everything for you.'

Deirdre rolled her eyes.

'I don't know what I'd do without you, Kathleen,' she said.

'Such nonsense. You lie still. I'll be back in a jiffy. Goodbye, Richard. You stay with Deirdre.'

She passed through the kitchen, saying: 'I'm going to the priest now.'

'Good,' said Julia, who was exhibiting a new respect. 'I'm making a sponge pudding for eight. That should give her a good feed. The Neelans will only pick at it. They'll have drink taken, if I know them.'

Kathleen went into her room, closed the door, and sat on the bed for a moment to calm her trembling nerves. Her sister's predicament was only a second chance reason for her appointment with Father Hanna. It was a vital chapter in her life. It had all been like a book and she could hardly believe it.

The first hint had come on the morning after the night at the Manhattan, when she had gone to Mass with Finola and Julia Byrne, and Paddy with his father had appeared to be even more distant than usual. This could have had one of two meanings, but all was made appallingly clear several days later when Paddy came to her in the garden, as she was hanging out the Master's socks on the line, looking shyer than ever. He told her that he and Finola had fallen for each other, and explained his extraordinary behaviour by saying that Kathleen had taught him the attraction of girls for the first time, and Finola had appeared on the scene almost at once. They were going with Mick to England, after Christmas. Finola was not sure if she would marry him. She wanted to 'look around' in England for a while.

It was not for Kathleen to tell him what that might mean, and in any case she was dumbstruck, and shut herself in her room, and refused to speak to Julia Byrne, who said: 'I told you so, I warned you!' In the end she went to the priest, who was like a saint to her. He said it so happened that Mr Trench had just approached him, and explained that with his son leaving he wanted to find a nice girl and marry again.

At first she had been terrified. But then she was filled with hope. She remembered that Paddy had always seemed to be too good-looking for her. Mr Trench was elderly, but he was more her style: cheerful, respectable, and kindly. Her experience with Paddy had shown her that she was very capable of love.

They were to meet at six.

She had watched him at Mass and found herself blushing. Soon afterwards she was blushing for a different reason. She could not believe that her gentle adviser was the same man thundering in the pulpit against her own sister. Finola had taken it much more calmly.

At the same time if what the priest said of Paddy was true, as it must be, then she was lucky to have escaped. If Finola was prepared for damnation, there was nothing she could do about it.

Now suddenly the chance to achieve the opposite for Deirdre had come like a sign. So, too, had Mr Trench's appeal to the priest. She had prayed, and these were the answers, and they were a lot more than she had bargained for.

Kathleen was perplexed by the difficulty of giving herself the right appearance for both Father Hanna and Mr Trench. She awarded the victory to the priest. On his account she decided to forgo the cosmetics in the cake-tin under the bed, and the black dress with the large red roses which she had bought especially for the Manhattan Ballroom and would now like to have worn as a symbol of recovery. She took off her cap and apron and put on a black coat over her plain black dress. She would never have dreamed of owning an umbrella, but chose the good excuse of the weather to tie a gay blue and yellow scarf on her head.

When she stepped out into the darkness, the soft, mysterious Irish rain was so heavy that she had to gasp for breath.

On the drive she was suddenly illuminated, and the Jaguar came purring up behind her.

Tom stopped, and, hearing that she was going to Father Hanna's, invited her, without seeking Moira's opinion, to sit in the back.

Behind them, they could hear her breathing heavily, in curious harmony with the windscreen-wiper. Moira was certain that her visit, and her condition, had something to do with the morning's sermon, but did not believe that Kathleen could possibly be one of the guilty parties. A more likely candidate was her flirtatious sister, under the corrupting influence of Grania Agerton-Willy. Father Hanna was the only person with any standards, or sense, in the whole community. She must invite him to dinner again and discuss the matter, whatever it was.

Since the girl was in the car with them, and engaged upon some project that was giving her the jitters, it made her curiously like a human being. Moira was not accustomed to thinking of the serv-ants in that light. However, she was not going to demean herself by conversing with the creature, and they drove the short way down the hill in silence, Tom dreaming all the time of Edenmore.

Muttering 'thank-yous', Kathleen got out and went off quickly towards Father Hanna's house whose lower windows shone brightly.

Tom drove on down the hill, made a complete turn in Mr

Cullen's monster car park, and drove up the hill again. They had to cross the mountains in the direction of Bray.

'You didn't have to go out of your way,' said Moira. 'We could have left her at our gate.'

'Charity, my dear, charity,' said Tom. 'The tinkling cymbals and so on and what have you. It's very wet.'

'I don't give a damn about your tinkling cymbals. *I* have to deal with them when they get ideas above their station.'

She never felt at ease in his Jaguar. He always seemed to be driving on the wrong side of the road.

At length, indeed, someone hooted behind, and he had to move over. They were passed by a Vauxhall, and she recognised its single occupant.

'That was him!' she exclaimed. 'That was him! Did you see?'

'See what? I saw nothing.'

He hardly seemed to be there under his camel-hair coat and great black hat: it was difficult to get through to the small person inside.

'Price-Jones,' she said, 'Price-Jones. She must have asked him. Now d'you see? Now d'you see? Oh, I'll have a thing or two to say to him if I get the chance.'

'There are other possible destinations across the mountains.'

'Don't you believe it!'

'If you have any intention of disrupting my business projects you had better forget it now,' he said, puffing through his cigarette so that red ashes flew about and she had to sweep them off her lap, giving a little cry of surprise.

'Ah, your business! I don't give a damn about it.'

'That's unfortunate, since you are my wife.'

'You see Brendan. Leave the rest to me.'

But after a long silence, she found that her mind was running solely on Charlie, and on the last time she had come this way. In the quiet and boredom of the mountains, she had suddenly one afternoon found herself tempted to an act that came close to lunacy. She had driven towards Bray, and gone slowly past the gate of Finlandia, compelled by the ludicrous dream that Norah was out, the servants departed, and Charlie home alone from work, suffering from some indisposition. As the worst of luck would have it, the house had turned out to be a desperate erection like a glass box, with windows so large that she saw Norah clearly through one and the servants through another, and was not at all sure that she herself had escaped detection. She had quickly returned home, depressed, ashamed and angry.

'I expect Norah's dressed to the nines,' she said, breaking the strained silence, 'and the house done up like nothing on earth. I wonder is it very modern or not.'

Everything was ready. Norah stood at the sitting-room window, hesitating to release the bamboo curtain. She was looking tall, brown and handsome this evening, in an expensive creation by Dan Lavelle: black and simple, based on a design by Balmain that she had come across when passing the long afternoon with *Vogue*. The reason she hesitated was that, even through the raindrops, the view was attractive: Bray's circle of twinkling lights following the sea round to the great black mound of Bray Head. The mainspring of its attraction was that it might well have been Cannes or any Riviera town as seen at night from the hills inland. It was very different when you descended and gave it a closer inspection.

She released the bamboo, and pressing another button sent the black and primrose curtain across it, thus assisting the hidden heating which had already brought the room to a high temperature. Charlie was seated in his elegant suit in the big scarlet chair, being unable to sit in either of the inverted hats because yesterday he had made his first tentative appearance with the Bray Harriers. He had used the mechanism attached to its arm to turn on the television and the B.B.C. news.

Thirty-four people had been killed in self-government clashes in Africa. Several thousand million pounds were to be spent on defence against the hydrogen bomb. In a bank robbery at Fulham, a police constable had been shot dead. A small boy had been stabbed thirty-three times in Hampstead, and a young woman had been found, stripped, raped and decapitated, in Bayswater.

He switched it off and she at once permitted Stanley Black to seep out from the hidden loudspeakers: soft, sophisticated and party-like. 'The lights of London town were upside down. Poor, puzzled moon, he wore a frown . . .'

Alfredo and Angelina had learned it, through familiarity, and Norah could hear them in the kitchen, at the end of the corridor, singing about the 'pozzled' moon.

She strolled about, making certain of everything. Charlie had this gift—or failing—of being incredibly, infuriatingly, at ease. She could give the impression of calm, she knew, but it was a deception. Of course he had seen to the preparation of the champagne, and would indeed serve it very well, and there his responsibility ended.

'I dislike this waiting,' she said. 'I suppose they'll all be late. They're never anything else in this country.'

'There's no hurry,' he said.

He was cleaning his nails with a nail-file.

'The boys will soon be home. We should really have waited for Vernon. He would have enjoyed it.'

'You miss him, don't you?'

'Yes. I do," she replied, looking at him in surprise.

'I miss Andrew.'

Astonished by these human sentiments, she tried to concentrate on all that she had done, with Alfredo and Angelina. The tall green glasses for the champagne were on the 'cello and double-bass tables. Behind the glass wall, the heatproof glass table, with the crimson plush chairs all around it, bore a brilliant display of Angelina's Italian canapés. Norah had set little red candles amidst the plates, as well as an array of bottles for Charlie's friends who were incapable of appreciating champagne. The lighting was altogether most attractive, particularly the glowing red shade just above her famous father-in-law's I.R.A. badge on the wall, with Vernon's seagull-feather decoration around it. Instead of the voodoo figure on the television set she had placed a vase of yellow chrysanthemums, and with the bamboos and rubber plants cutting off the hall they had that feeling of nature

within and without which both she and Charlie recognised to be
basic to modern living.

She had arranged that Alfredo would lay out the ladies' coats
on their mink-lined bed, and the men's in the boys' rooms. The
early arrivals would be catered for by the outstretched arms of
Fergus O'Toole's sculptured beggarman in the hall: a haggard,
pitiful creature, but a fine work of art.

'God knows what they're going to think of it,' she said. 'It'll be
twenty years before most of them appreciate that this is the way
to live.'

'Perhaps your foreign friend will make up for them.'

'Who do you mean by that?'

'Your Hugo. I hear that you've been eating out a lot lately.'

'Any objections?'

'No, no.'

'It must be a little surprising for you that the Neelans are coming after all.'

'Ha, ha. Yes, that's true.'

'Is he buying Edenmore?'

'I don't know.'

'Father Hanna was useless. You should have let me talk to the
Major.'

'Maybe. We forgot that he was your type.'

'He's a lot more my "type" than some of the people coming this
evening.'

'I'm sorry about that. But I have the same trouble.'

Her real responsibility was the people. In spite of what he said,
Charlie took them as they came, so to speak, while she worked.
What she had to work at chiefly was mixing her own cultivated
friends in with his guests, who were nothing of the kind. It was
not a question of mere introductions, because, this being Dublin,
they all knew each other already: it was rather a question of in-
ducing mutual suffering. Charlie appeared unaware of the difficulty, which was great considering that most of his men friends
were cattle-dealers, farmers, trainers and bookies. They were ox-

like, with thick necks and double chins; of peasant origin and curiously Germanic-looking; Bavarian perhaps. Their faces were beet-red. They were prosperous and horribly cheerful. With contrasting dark suits they wore nominally brown shoes of a curiously brilliant orange tint, giving an impression of country life, with plenty of time to do extraordinary things with shoe-polish. Otherwise they had no polish, and alarmed her when they took her hand in a strong fat paw, and shook and bellowed at some inexplicable jest, turning from crimson to scarlet. Four such gentlemen had been invited. It gave her almost physical pain to think of how they would react to Finlandia. In the case of two, she knew already: they had come to her small dinner party, and with Charlie's assistance nearly demolished the place. One of these gentlemen had been concerned with the famous Seamus in the fight for freedom, and although peppered with bullets had scarcely noticed it.

She had apologised for them in advance to Hugo, with whom she had been lunching nearly every day. He was thriving on being a storm centre. He had come to rely on her, speaking incessantly of his domestic tribulations and giving her cause to feel greatly flattered. She was not sure what he intended, or where it would proceed.

The bell rang, and past the rubber plants and bamboos, through the glass hall-door, she saw the slender figure of Dan Lavelle, and she felt an immediate sense of relief.

Alfredo was there before her. He was a gaunt man, by contrast with his plump wife, and greatly resembled the hall sculpture. He invited Dan Lavelle to leave his umbrella in the shelter of the porch, and laid his short mackintosh across the beggarman's arms.

'Darling,' said Dan, and he kissed her hand.

He was small, youthful, lively, good-humoured, and elegant in a dark suit with cuffs and a waistcoat with lapels; perhaps a little superficial, but one would certainly never have guessed that he was the son of a haberdasher in Kilkenny.

'I had to come early to see how it looked,' he said, referring to her costume. 'I feared I might lose you in the crush. My, my, but it's a *succès fou!*'

'Do you like it?'

'Or rather I should say that you make it so. Good evening, Charles. Isn't she a couturier's dream?'

'It's a nice dress. It ought to be at the price.'

'Oh, isn't he an old grumpy! When are you going to come and model for me, dear? But what an enchanting room!' he added, and gazed all around him in admiration. 'It quite takes the breath away. He's not such a philistine as he makes out, our Charles, is he. He's really one of us.'

'It's all Norah's doing,' said Charlie.

'That's not strictly true,' said Norah.

'Now let's not argue, dears, I can see the work of both hands. It really is quite, quite enchanting!'

'You *are* kind, Dan,' said Norah, in delight, and she saw Alfredo admitting one of the Bavarians through the hall door; a man like a red bull. It was a wealthy cattle-dealer named Andy Dolan, followed by his wife and an unknown gentleman who looked to be about four feet tall.

Her happiness evaporated.

'Ha, ha,' said Charlie. 'If it isn't the bold Andy and the lovely Molly!'

The wife, Molly, was blonde and rather haggard, but she had good features and was undeniably attractive. It was extraordinary how such monstrous men always had such good-looking wives. Was money all that tempting?

Dan knew them. He had been an uneasy member of their party at the last Louth Hunt Ball, because Molly had been one of his first customers. However, when she took off her camel-hair coat she was seen to be wearing a brown dress that was certainly not his.

When they had all shaken hands, she said:

'D'you know Terry Duggan, our famous—or should I say infamous—jockey?'

The dapper little man bowed to them.

An uninvited guest. This was a good start. Norah wondered how many more of them there were going to be. She suddenly felt cold with anger and said to Dan: 'Do come and see my bedroom,' and noted the bold Andy's small eyes open wide with surprise.

'My God, it's rather weird, isn't it?' she heard Molly Dolan saying as they crossed the hall and went along the corridor.

Dan was ecstatic over the contemporary crucifix. He stroked the mink edges of the bedspread. When they went into the bathroom he adored the octopus groping for the bath-taps; and although she was very pleased, she was listening all the time to the rising noise in the sitting-room, which was already beginning to drown Stanley Black.

Had Hugo arrived?

They passed Alfredo carrying a bundle of overcoats and mackintoshes down to the bedrooms.

About twenty people had appeared in that short time. Charlie had deftly opened two bottles of champagne. The round, ever-gay figure of Angelina was in their midst, distributing the tall green glasses and handing round the canapés. Both the Callinans and the Brophys were there, pretending to appreciate her ancient pistols and hunting-horns on the wall.

'A cunning arrangement, a cunning arrangement,' said a large Bavarian who she remembered was the old I.R.A. man. He was looking straight at Vernon's feather-work and she dared him to make a comment.

She talked about Cannes with her former companions, and then did so again with David Keely, James Larkin and Kevin Barry, who confessed to subsequent hilarious adventures in Paris, but refused to divulge what they were.

She was more pleased to see Terence Keogh, whose grey head towered above Dan Lavelle. 'You're looking even more handsome than my portrait, my dear,' he said.

The Neelans were arriving. Moira was quite pretty in a black dress, which was however covered with little bows, in noticeable contrast to her own. 'My goodness, but you've done wonders, Norah!' she said. 'I've never seen anything like it. Isn't she clever, Tom?'

'A quite remarkable effort,' said Tom. 'Altogether a case of the old *mirabile dictu*. It makes you put on your own, as you might say, thinking-cap. The cap *à pensée*. The kappa, beta, gama, eh? Look to one's own guns, or pistols is perhaps the correct term for what I see appended to the wall there, if my eyes don't deceive me. Of earlier date I presume,' he said, taking Norah suddenly by the elbow, massaging it, and murmuring conspiratorially, 'than the conflict involving our famous father-in-law. Eh? Am I right?'

'Oh yes. No connection,' she replied, wondering whether the jest demanded a response, and feeling the pain ebbing out of her elbow as it was suddenly released.

'But his badge is there,' she said.

'Oh, oh,' said Tom. 'Not forgotten? Oh, very suitable, very decorative, very *comme il faut*. A feathery concoction, one might say, made with loving hands. Your own tribute, I take it?'

'Well, Vernon's really.'

'Ah, ha. *Filius mirabilis.*'

Moira flinched and moved away. It always became worse at parties, or when he was meeting new people, or for any reason growing excited. He was a shy person, really. No one knew it except her. She saw Charlie approaching with a green glass, and Tom's quotations put her in mind of a Greek god approaching with a vase.

'How's the form?' he said.

She accepted the glass, and exclaimed: 'Gracious, it's champagne!'

'Nothing else would be good enough.'

'Oh, go along with you!' she said.

He plucked a small yellow chrysanthemum from a display

close at hand, and before she knew what was happening had inserted it in the brooch on her front. It obscured a rather pretty shamrock in mock emeralds and must look terrible.

'A tribute from an admirer,' he said.

He was obviously tight. He was god-like, but somehow not quite the person that she had driven all the way across the mountains to see.

However, there was such a crush that no one could observe her odd corsage, and a noise, and a party spirit; and she laughed and was happy. She noted Ann and Brendan, past a number of heads, because there was a slight disturbance going on. The fat woman in a white coat, who must be one of Norah's Italians, was exclaiming at Brendan: 'Orange squash! You want orange squash!'

It was not going to be easy for Tom to take Brendan aside.

Patrick also had seen Ann, but only distantly through the rubber plants, because on arrival he had been halted immediately inside the hall-door by 'Teeth' Murphy and Mrs Murphy. He was not sure whether she had seen him, and was far too excited to listen, though he was aware that 'Teeth' was telling him the true story of how the Holy Name had come to be altered to 'By Gum'; a tale in which Church and State appeared to be equally and deviously involved.

The subject had been provoked by the presence of Lorrimer. Indeed the whole hallway was going over the night's events once again, and 'Twitcher' Doyle was recounting how he had made the Dublin *bon mot*: 'O God, O Manchester!'

Norah saw all this and took Hugo away to show him the bathroom. She had the feeling that it was beginning to go beyond her, in a way known of old, and had counted at least ten people she had never laid eyes on before.

Hugo was wearing a blue bow-tie with white spots and was looking altogether like a person of distinction.

Following her along the corridor, he was saying in a voice to awaken the back of the stalls: 'Veronica would have adored this!'

She could not conceive why the person of whose peccadilloes

she had heard almost too much was now being missed all of a sudden.

Their way was momentarily barred by the only parliamentary representative who went to plays and read books. He was questioning Alfredo, who was telling him that at home there was much poverty, whereas in this country it was all so very different.

She had the disturbing impression that Alfredo was not sober.

They stood in the doorway of the bedroom, and Hugo said: 'But such variety! I've just been talking to the art dealer . . .'

'Oh yes. Lawrence Hurley. That's mink.'

'Yes, and a jockey, a couturier and a cattle-dealer. And what is more, they all appeared to know each other quite well. And the cattle-dealer had views on the moral implications of our unfortunate play. Well, I mean, in no other city on earth, my dear. . . .'

'Quite.'

'Well, certainly not in one house! It's perfect. Veronica would be in seventh heaven.'

'Do you not like this room?'

'Oh, delightful, delightful.'

He was equally unspecific in his admiration of the boys' rooms and the bathroom. She thought that he was probably the sort of person who favoured Louis Quinze and frightful chandeliers. There were a few things she could teach Hugo.

'That painter fellow, Mr Keogh, apologised to me for spending the night in my dressing-room. I had no idea what he was talking about.

'How extraordinary.'

They looked into the kitchen, which was large, airy and white, with a big table at the centre covered in red Formica, and red curtains to match around the huge windows. Brendan Smith was standing there in an uncomfortable way, and Angelina was furiously squeezing out an orange and shouting Italian imprecations.

Norah doubted if she was sober either, and wondered how this could possibly have occurred.

On returning, she was alarmed by the bedlam: by the explosions of laughter from the red-faced Bavarians and the bangs from the champagne bottles, which Charlie seemed to have relinquished, for they were being opened indiscriminately and she saw one spouting forth on to the sitting-room carpet. It led her eyes in the direction of Alfredo, who was on his knees sweeping up the remains of one of the green glasses into a pan. All the guests were shouting; most noticeably Terence Keogh, who was accusing Lawrence Hurley of foisting off paint dribbles from the gutter upon the new bourgeoisie. He looked wild and almost uncontrollable. The party was not hers. It had been timed for six to eight, and it was now eight and no one was departing. The house was hers no more. They had taken over.

Close to despair, she turned a knob on the wall, doubled the volume of Stanley Black, and cried out: 'Would you like to dance in the hall?'

She had the notion that it might calm, silence, and civilise them.

'Have you seen Brendan anywhere?'

She heard the anxious voice of Ann Neelan, who was standing with Patrick Price-Jones.

'Yes. In the kitchen,' she replied distractedly. 'Please dance.'

'Brendan doesn't,' said Ann.

She did not know what the girl was talking about, but saw her move on to the parquet with Patrick. Others followed. Charlie was already gliding about the hall with Moira Neelan. For some reason it annoyed Norah. He was undeniably the best-looking man in the room. Patrick was handsome, but young. Indeed, it struck her that only three members of the entire company were under forty; although the quietude of island life had kept her friends, with perhaps slightly greyer hair, looking exactly the same for the past twenty years. All the same, emigration had done its worst, perhaps even more noticeably here than among the lower orders. They were an ageing society.

'Let's dance,' she said to Hugo; and after a few turns she was aware of calm again. Without her saying a word, he seemed to have understood exactly how she was feeling.

Moira did not notice Patrick and Ann together; nor did she observe Tom, who was doing his jigging step with Molly Dolan.

'I haven't seen you since Sorrento,' she said.

'Missed me?' Charlie inquired.

'Gracious, no. Why should I? Well, I must say, it's a most unusual house.'

'I'm sure Tom disapproves. It's a long way from his builders and contractors.'

'Oh, now, that's enough.'

She meant it, more strongly than he knew. She was quite piqued by his remark.

'Ah, forgive me,' he said.

After a few moments she did.

'Signor Neelan! Signor Neelan!' Alfredo was rushing about in an excitable way; and she saw Tom disappearing with him.

'What was all that about, I wonder?'

'Possibly the telephone,' Charlie replied. 'We've a pink telephone, you know.'

'Oh, I can imagine!'

He laughed, and gave her a fright.

Tom was back, with his hat and coat. He looked dazed.

'I must go,' he said. 'Most urgent call. Most urgent. Are you coming?'

'What?'

'Are you coming?'

It was difficult. Some of the guests were saying good-bye to Norah. Charlie was not offering to drive her home.

'You might tell me what it is!'

'I can't,' said Tom.

She had never heard him using so few words. She began to feel afraid.

'All right, I'll get my coat.'

Brendan stopped her in the corridor, asking: 'Where's Ann?'

'I don't know. I don't know.'

'She was with that Price-Jones.'

'What!'

'Hurry!' shouted Tom.

She went out after him, through the hall door.

Norah said a bewildered good-bye to them in the porch under the ferro-concrete curvilinear roof on which the rain was thundering. It was cool after the extreme heat inside. Hugo came out behind her and they stood for a while in silence.

'I wonder what on earth was wrong with the Neelans,' she said.

Something else was wrong in the house. Stanley Black had turned to rock 'n' roll—to one of Andrew's records—and she saw through the glass Molly Dolan and an unknown man, in a whirling movement, falling straight through the bamboos and rubber plants, with shouts.

'My God!' she said, and hurried inside.

The noise was maddening. She rushed down the corridor to Andrew's room, where the uproar originated from the radiogram. There were five people on the bed. She switched off the music.

She stepped out and was nearly knocked over by the heavy form of Angelina, who ran past, shrieking, into the kitchen, followed by Kevin Barry with an ancient pistol and James Larkin blowing peals on a hunting-horn. They pursued her round and round the kitchen table. Norah heard the sound of vomiting in the bathroom and looked inside. An unknown man raised his head from the basin, and gesturing at her wallpaper, said: 'I must apologise, madam. It was all these bloody fish.'

Distraught and furious, she went into her bedroom, which was crowded, and pulled a coat out of the wardrobe and strode down the corridor.

Molly Dolan and her partner had extricated themselves from the bent and broken plants. Coats had been thrown on the floor and two of her red candles fixed to the beggarman's hands.

'Where's the music?' someone shouted at her.

Terence Keogh was standing before her portrait, looking wild and mad.

'Note the extreme subtlety of the flesh tints, ladies and gentlemen,' he was saying. 'And the delicate brilliance of the lipstick. . . .'

'For God's sake, take me out of this!' she said to Hugo, who was standing there, numb and confused.

She went to the sitting-room to tell Charlie that it would all be his responsibility now.

He was among a group of admirers looking up at David Keeley, who was standing on high in one of the inverted hats. He was singing 'The Old Clockmaker' and leering at the ladies in his audience.

' "Clocks to repair," he would shout day and night,
In an hour and five minutes he'd have your clock right.'

'Let's go,' she said.

The sound of applause and cheering followed them as they went out into the rain; and rock 'n' roll music poured forth from Finlandia, accompanied by occasional peals from a hunting-horn, as they got into Hugo's hired car.

chapter eighteen

'I don't know that I should be going,' Moira was saying as Tom drove the Jaguar out of the gate. 'Ann's disappeared with that Price-Jones—as I warned you, but you wouldn't listen, oh no!'

'This is of more importance, I regret to inform you.'

'More important? Well, what is it, what is it, in the name of goodness?'

'That is what we are hoping—or should I say fearing—to learn. It was very noisy, and Kathleen on the phone was so excited— indeed, curiously enough, I might almost say exhilarated—that it was exceedingly difficult to hear.'

He was driving very fast on the right-hand side of the road. The headlights swept the old walls and bramble hedges. The rain struck the windscreen in savage gusts.

'Well, don't kill us,' she said, gripping the door handle. 'What *did* you hear?'

'One of the householders would appear to have put in a phone-call of an anonymous and vulgar nature, unsuited to the sensibility of our Kathleen, followed by calls from our national newspapers.'

'About what?' she asked, beginning to be afraid again.

'The houses. It would seem that the rain is coming through.'

They were going up the hills. A man on a bicycle with no lights was struggling in front of them. He must be soaked.

'What does that mean exactly?'

'I should have thought it was plain.'

'Ah, for God's sake, Tom! How does it concern us? The houses are sold, aren't they? Why do we have to go racing through the night?'

'We built them; or rather my colleague did, with my support. I very much doubt if *he's* putting in an appearance.'

'Quite! Why should he? It's their own look-out.'

'In law, yes, *in jure*. But, in fact, I'm concerned to know whether I'm losing my reputation, and whether it may perhaps be saved. Our newspapers are extremely active on the rare occasions when something happens here.'

They were silent. She recalled that she had once given a woman selling oranges the contents of her handbag to keep Tom's name, and a tiny insignificant collision, out of the papers. She also remembered that he had said it only needed a new *'scandale'* to remove Lorrimer from the press.

They had been driving for about twenty minutes, but it seemed much shorter; and the outward journey had been so long. She felt cold.

'Is the heater on?'

He did not hear.

The rain was relentless. It had assumed a new, hostile, hateful character.

She glanced at him. He had put on the black hat so hastily that it was over one ear. His manner had always made it difficult to know his feelings, but she thought that he was very distressed.

'Did you expect anything like this?'

'Of course not.'

'I'm sorry. I didn't mean ... What are you going to do, Tom? We're nearly there.'

'Talk to them. You might be able to help.'

She had once thought of helping; calling on the wives, asking if the kitchens were satisfactory; but not like this.

They were up at the top of the village, passing the gate of their own house. The light was on outside O'Sullivan's, and all the lights outside Cullen's. The avenue to Edenmore was dark. If this was serious, she supposed that Edenmore would have to be abandoned. What would they do?

As the wall ended, the houses began. They looked the same:

semi-detached, red-brick, with bow-windowed fronts, and the lights on. Perhaps there were more lights than usual.

Under a concrete bus shelter, erected especially for the convenience of the estate, stood about a dozen youths who appeared to pay particular attention as Tom slowly approached. They were close to the window. Moira recognised young Trench, the son of the Edenmore gardener.

'It's the Jag all right,' said one of them. 'It's Neelan, the dirty sh——. There he is!'

Suddenly there were shouts, and the faces had come nearer.

'You bastard!' Moira heard.

'What the devil!' said Tom.

He accelerated, turned sharply and went down one of the cul-de-sacs. She looked through the rear window, but they were not following. The rain had its advantages.

Tom stopped. He took off his hat and placed it in his lap, and wiped his face with a handkerchief. His hand was trembling.

'Oh, God, what are we doing here?' she said. 'Let's go home.'

It was silent, except for the rain. The houses seemed innocent and normal, although there were lights on in a number of upper windows.

'I have to know what all this is about,' he said, putting on his hat and opening his door.

'Don't leave me here.'

'Come with me.'

They went up to the door of the nearest house. The top half of it was stained-glass panels with a light behind them. Tom pressed the bell, and at length a shadowy form approached.

A tired-looking man in shirt-sleeves and braces opened the door. He was gaunt and lined, and aged about fifty.

'Good evening,' said Tom. 'My name is Neelan . . .'

'It's what?'

'Neelan . . .'

'Oh, is it, is it! By God, it's a wonder you've the nerve to show your face around here.'

'I understood there's been some trouble . . .'

'Trouble! There's been trouble all right. You little swine. I'd . . .'

'Jim?'

A woman's voice was calling down the stairs.

'That's my wife. You ask *her* if there's been trouble.'

'Who is it, Jim?'

'It's Mr Bloody Neelan come to pay a visit!' he shouted.

'Might we step inside?' said Tom, moving past him. 'My wife is getting wet.'

The woman appeared on the landing. She was large and strongly built, and much younger than her husband; tired too, with unkempt hair, in a dirty dress. Moira thought she was pregnant.

'I remember you all right, though you may not remember me, Mr Fine-Phrases Neelan,' she shouted down the stairs. 'Well, the whole country's going to know about you now. Wait till the Guards hear of it. You're going to jail for this, my man!'

'Might I see what's happened?'

'Oh, by all means. Come on up. Let herself and her swank clothes see it too. Show her where the money came from!'

They followed the woman up the stairs, with the husband behind.

'The whole estate's flooded,' he said. 'The same dirty story. And it's going to be told too. There's a gang of reporters and photographers going round the place. Where's that dirty rat of a builder of yours?'

'That's what I was wondering,' said Tom.

'By God, I'd like to get my hands on him!'

Off the top landing were two drably furnished bedrooms, a nursery and a bathroom. In the parents' bedroom three small children, in pyjamas, wrapped in rugs, were seated before the gas-fire. Around them was a steaming circle of bedclothes. The double bed had been moved aside and drops were falling from the ceiling into saucepans on the floor. Across the whole of one wall the beige paper with the flowered edge was soaking. In places it bulged out from the wall and appeared to be holding a quantity of water behind it.

Moira met the staring eyes of the children. She could not conceive how Tom had permitted this to happen. Nor could she think of what to say.

'There's your fine houses, Mr Neelan!' said the woman.

'Very distressing,' said Tom.

'Ha, ha, distressing!' said the husband. 'Well, I'm going to see it's made bloody well distressing for you too.'

'That won't be necessary.'

'I'm terribly sorry for you,' said Moira to the wife. 'I know my husband had no idea that the builder . . .'

'Ah, save your breath! What happens when these three go down with pneumonia, tell me that!'

'Oh, I'm sure they'll be all right. They look awfully well . . .'

'You're damn sure about everything, aren't you?' said the husband.

'That'll do,' said Tom.

He led the way into the nursery, which was the same. The wallpaper with the rabbits on it was soaking. The bedroom of the two older children resembled that of the parents, with the beds moved aside and the water dripping into pots and pans.

'Who's going to pay for it all?' demanded the husband. 'Tell me that, Mr Blasted Neelan. No one's insured here.'

'I don't know. I don't know.'

The hall-door bell was ringing as they came down the stairs.

'Some more of your damn friends, I suppose, come to see the show,' said the husband, who was walking in front.

He opened the door and a crowd came into the hall; first a gaggle of photographers and then a rush of furious men and women. Moira, who was on the stairs, was suddenly terrified. Tom was being shouted at and pushed about. A man was roaring obscenities at him. He was bundled into the room off the hall, and she saw him surrounded by men with note-books. Camera bulbs were flashing. He seemed to be mumbling and muttering and not answering anything.

'Leave him alone!' she heard herself commanding. No one noticed except a woman close at hand who shook a fist in her face and said: 'May God forgive you and your like!'

The husband was holding a furious argument with the rougher members of the crowd, pushing them towards the door, and shouting: 'This is my house. Where the hell are the Guards?'

With his help the hall was slowly cleared, and the reporters, evidently satisfied, began to move out.

'I'm afraid your car's banjaxed, old man,' said one of them. 'The lads down at the shelter, I believe. We'd give you a lift, only we're full up.'

'Oh,' said Tom, without understanding.

When they came out the crowd had dispersed. They saw at once, under the lamplight, that the tyres were flat and had been fiercely slashed with a knife.

He was silent.

'Oh, Tom,' she said.

The husband was standing behind them in the doorway, watching with satisfaction.

'Might I use your telephones?' Tom asked.

'There's no telephone yet in these houses, as you know damn well.'

'Oh yes. I forgot.'

'You'd better walk,' he said, and slammed the door.

'Come on,' said Tom.

He took her hand, and they walked back to the main road, crossing over so that the bus shelter was some distance away. The youths were still there, and a voice said: 'Walking home, Neelan? Too bad!'

Something hit the pavement near them: a stone presumably.

A moment later a black car with 'Gardai' illuminated on the top came rushing past them and went on to the houses.

'I wonder where they've been,' said Tom. 'Looking for me, I expect.'

'Shall we go back? One of them must have a knife.'

'No, no. He'll have got rid of it. It'll do in the morning. I've had enough tonight.'

She held his hand more tightly.

The rain was blinding.

'We can't walk all the way in this, Tom,' she said.

'We'll go in to Edenmore,' he said, 'and phone for a cab.'

She thought she could not face it, but there seemed to be no alternative.

That particular project was gone. Everything was gone. She could scarcely guess at his feelings. She was afraid he might be broken by it.

'Why would the police be calling?'

'Routine, I think they term it.'

'You said there'd be nothing against you?'

'I don't think so. I'll have to see our solicitor.'

The Murrough-Bryants' wall had begun, and went on and on. The rain had made her face icy cold, and from closing her eyes against it she had a splitting pain across her forehead. She was wearing a little black hat, and it must be ruined; and a black coat with a Persian-lamb collar, which was sopping wet against her cheek. She was only now comprehending fully what they had encountered, coming straight from a party and dancing; and with comprehension came tears. She was starting to cry and tried to restrain it, but it did not seem to matter. The tears mingled with the rain on her face.

Tom was aware of it, because he squeezed her hand.

'*Nil desperandum*,' he said. '*Nil desperandum*.'

When they turned at last into the Murrough-Bryants' gate she saw the light on in the gardener's gate lodge, and was tempted to go in, to sit in the warmth.

The drive was inky black, and the rain was making a loud clattering among the leaves of the rhododendrons.

As they went up the steps and were waiting for someone to open the door, Moira thought that this was a dreadful mistake. They would have to confess everything to these people; and Grania Agerton-Willy would see her looking like a tramp.

Finola switched on the light, opened the door, and said: 'Gracious!'

She was doubly alarmed because these were the people she had left for a higher wage.

'It's all right, Finola,' said Tom. 'Is anyone in?'

'Yes, they are.'

They entered the hall, and Finola proceeded heavily to the drawing-room. They stood near the great empty fireplace, and pools of water began to form at their feet. Moira was troubled by the armour and the deers' heads. They had never been here before.

Grania came hurrying out, in her black shirt and red trousers. She had been playing patience. Hilda had gone to town to have her portrait painted and had not returned, and her father was in the room upstairs writing an article.

'Oh, my dear!' she said, going up to Moira.

'I'm afraid we're a fright,' said Moira hastily. 'I'm very sorry. We've no right coming in like this. We just wanted to phone for a taxi.'

'I see. But it would take time, coming from town. I can't let you stay in these things, my dear, you'll catch your death. You come along upstairs with me and I'll find you some things right away. And Mr Neelan, I'll ask my father . . .'

'No, no, please. If I just get off this hat and coat.'

'Finola, take Mr Neelan's hat and coat to the drying-room. And perhaps you'd go in to the fire and give yourself a stiff whisky, while I bring your wife upstairs.'

'You are most kind.'

'Nonsense. Now come along, Mrs Neelan.'

Moira went like a child. She felt like crying or laughing with relief that the worst was over. On the stairs she began:

'It was the houses. We went to the houses and it was terrible . . .'

'Never mind, dear, never mind. Excuse me,' Grania added, on the landing, and she went into the Major's room.

He was seated at the Sheraton writing-desk.

'Father, Mr and Mrs Neelan are here, absolutely soaked through to the skin. He's down by the fire. Would you go and see if he wants any dry clothes?'

'Right,' said the Major after a moment.

In Grania's room, Moira took off her coat and hat, and shoes and stockings. The rain had penetrated inside her coat and her dress was wet too. Grania persuaded her to take it off. She stood there in a pink slip, feeling no embarrassment in face of Grania's confident and easy manner.

Grania was looking in a wardrobe, privately trying to find a dress that would be large enough. She chose a brown one, with a belt that was expandable.

'This may be a little long, I'm afraid. But it's warm.'

'You're very kind. Honest, we didn't expect this at all!'

Moira stepped into it and found that it nearly reached her ankles, but she did not care.

'How on earth did it happen, my dear?' asked Grania, producing stockings and bedroom slippers, and handing Moira a towel to dry her wild-looking blonde hair.

'We were called away from the party to the houses, and they were all pouring water. That blasted builder of Tom's! And they pushed Tom about . . . reporters and all. And someone cut the tyres of his car.'

'Oh, my God!'

Moira was combing her hair in the mirror and saw tears in her red eyes.

'It'll all be in the papers . . .'

She stopped combing and began sobbing.

'He's ruined, ruined . . .'

Grania put an arm around her.

'There, there, my dear. I'm sure it won't be so bad.'

'It will. It will . . .'

'I'm sure he'll be able to deal with it. It's not his fault. My father will want to help. Shall we go down and talk to him? Let's do that. Shall we?'

'All right,' said Moira, controlling herself and borrowing Grania's handkerchief. 'I'm desperately sorry. You must think very poorly of me.'

'On the contrary,' said Grania. 'It's funny what brings people together, isn't it?'

They both smiled; Moira through tears.

In the drawing-room they found Tom seated by the fire, holding a large whisky and wearing the Major's socks and bedroom slippers. The Major, also holding a whisky, stood with his back to the mantelpiece, dwarfed by his week-end clothes, his old coat and corduroys.

Tom rose, and Grania said: 'Please sit down. I think you should have a brandy, Mrs Neelan. It'll do you good.'

She went over to the bottles on the old desk.

'Has Mr Neelan told you about this wretched piece of luck?'

'Yes, yes,' the Major replied. 'I'm very sorry indeed.'

'And the car slashed. What filthy people!'

'I'm afraid there's an element of savagery not far below the calm surface of Irish life.'

'It's worse luck for those people,' said Tom. 'It's my fault. I should have scrutinised my colleagues' credentials more thoroughly. I fear there's no point in our meeting in the morning, Major.'

He was gazing into the fire in a way that worried Moira.

'If that's so, we're in trouble too. I don't really know what we shall do.'

'Did your son come home from the party?' asked Moira, surprising them all by this change of subject.

'No. Not yet,' Grania replied.

'I was just wondering. He disappeared with our Ann, I believe.'

'Oh. Well, perhaps they'll turn up. In any case, you must stay to dinner.'

'Oh no, no, really, we wouldn't dream of it,' said Moira. 'I'd honestly like to get home straight away. Did you call a taxi, Tom?'

'No, I . . .'

'I'll drive you,' said the Major.

'Oh no, we couldn't . . .'

'Flanagan will do it, if you like, Father.'

'No, no. I'll take them, if I may have the Bentley.'

'Of course,' said Grania.

'But your clothes will still be wet, Mrs Neelan,' she added.

'It doesn't matter. I'd honestly like to get home, you know.'

'Yes, I understand. I'll have Finola put them in a suitcase for you. Or will you leave them?'

'No, I'll take them, thank you very much.'

Soon they had said good-bye to Grania, and the Major was driving them up the hill in the Bentley, with Moira beside him in an old tweed coat of Grania's and Tom in the back.

'I apologise for referring to my own troubles,' said the Major, 'but perhaps it will help to take your mind off yours. It's very unfortunate for me that I turned down that other offer.'

'Another offer, Major?' Tom inquired.

'Yes, by the priest. Father Hanna.'

'The priest!' exclaimed Moira.

'Yes, on behalf of the architect, Charlie Gerraty, and some religious order. I didn't care for the idea.'

'The priest, you say, and Gerraty?' said Tom.

'Yes. Isn't he a friend of yours? Surely he's told you about it by now?'

'Not a word,' said Moira, tight-lipped. She was beginning to remember things.

'Father Hanna seemed to be well informed about your intentions, and the price, and so on.'

'He was informed by Tom, in our own house,' said Moira. 'I can hardly believe it. And those Gerratys!'

They were in front of Hill View. The vista of Dublin's lights was obscured by cloud and rain. They said good night and profusely thanked the Major, who drove away.

Tom opened the door, and Moira went ahead in a daze, in a dress and coat reaching almost to her ankles. Kathleen, who was putting coal on the fire in the drawing-room, looked her over in astonishment, said 'Good evening, ma'am', and went quickly out.

The case was still in her hand. She put it on the sofa, opened it, and saw the damp black dress lying on top. Charlie's yellow chrysanthemum was still fixed into her brooch.

She took it out and flung it on the fire.

Tom, standing in the doorway, said: 'I think I'll just have tea and toast up in my room.'

'All right, Tom dear.'

She went across and put her arms around him and kissed him quickly on the cheek.

Kathleen had seen this from the far end of the hall. She went into the kitchen and said to Julia Byrne:

'The mistress is in somebody else's clothes, and they're kissing each other.'

'I thought as much,' said Julia Byrne. 'They've drink taken.'

Moira had followed Kathleen, to tell them that she would be having dinner alone.

'There were desperate phone-calls,' Kathleen said excitedly, 'and the Guards were here . . .'

'I know. I know.'

'I've got some great news,' Kathleen added, turning red. 'I'm to marry Mr Trench. I'll be leaving you before Christmas.'

'Leaving me?'

'Yes, ma'am. The priest arranged it.'

'The priest?'

'That's right,' said Julia Byrne. 'I've made a suet pudding. Will Himself not be having any?'

'What was that about the priest?'

An unknown voice was calling from the neighbouring bathroom.

Moira saw curious expressions on their faces, and went inside.

She observed nothing except the drying-stand, with sheets on it. But hearing a sound, she looked over it and saw an unknown woman lying in the bath with a dog on top of her. She screamed.

'It's all right, ma'am, its all right,' said Kathleen. 'It's my sister Deirdre. She's going to be a nun.'

'The priest arranged that too,' said Julia Byrne, with pride.

chapter nineteen

'This is crazy,' Ann said. 'What am I going to tell Brendan?'

They sat at a bar in a Bray hotel, made of bottle glass, lit redly from behind to match the red leather stools. Behind the white-coated barmen was a contemporary fresco, by a Sunday painter in the Port and Docks Board, showing scenes of Bray, with ladies carrying parasols along the esplanade. It was the modern part of an otherwise antique lounge, with Landseer's stag on one wall. The march of progress found the drinking departments leading all other domestic interiors in Ireland.

Behind a glass door they could see the residents, including six or seven priests, tucking in to high tea in a haze of blue indigo smoke from the kitchen, which carried a stench of fried food right into the lounge.

The lateness of this meal was presumably explained by the wedding reception which had been in progress here since three that afternoon. Men with tousled hair, in hired morning clothes, reeled about the place while their wives and girl friends sat in the chintz chairs admiring their powers of consumption. There was a perpetual motion of meetings, embracings, partings, joining up with others, parting and re-forming again, and sometimes a group would converge upon the bar. A few of the bolder girls, in frocks elaborately ornamented with buttons and bows, were upright among the men, joining in the general flirtation: arms around necks and a newly born love of one another. There was shouting and singing, and there were cries of 'That's enough from you, Matt Daly!' and 'What did you do with the cigs, Maureen?'

'We'll go back in a minute,' said Patrick. 'No one will have noticed.'

'You don't know Dublin!'

He had suggested standing out on the porch for a breath of air, and then on an impulse taken her hand and said: 'Come on,' and run with her to the car.

Perhaps the champagne had momentarily given him courage. He soon realised that they were not going to sit in the car and look at the sea. Some need for distraction and security had driven them straight into this bright and noisy place.

'I ought to. I've only been here about a month, I know, but it seems like years.'

'Has so much happened?' she asked, mockingly.

'Things have happened to me.'

'Oh?'

'I want to talk to the most beautiful girl in the room,' drooled one of the wedding-guests, suddenly placing a heavy hand on her shoulder and nearly pulling her off the stool.

'She doesn't want to talk to you,' said Patrick. 'Clear off.'

'I beg your pardon?'

'Clear off.'

'Go away,' said Ann.

'What damned inhospiddableble people,' he said, staggering away.

'How I hate it all,' she said quietly.

'The very first evening I arrived,' said Patrick, 'I found myself singing a solo in a large friendly group in the local. And I thought I was part of everything.'

'That's asking rather a lot, Patrick.'

'I suppose so. But one does want to be among contemporaries, to be at least a part of their society, enjoying the stimulus of company and work. Without that, it seems like years passing. Timeless. Interminable.'

'*I* told you that.'

'Yes, you did. The point is . . . I'm going back.'

She looked up suddenly.

'To London?'

'Yes. After Christmas.'

'To what?'

'Advertising. Oh, another firm.'

'I see . . . I'm sorry it's all been so pointless.'

'It hasn't.'

'In any case,' he said, 'everything's breaking up here. Tomorrow your father is buying Edenmore. Grandfather is going to take some little grey home by Dublin Bay he has his eye on. He pretends to like it. Getting to know him has been another of the gains here. I wish I thought Mother had gained in some way, but she's now planning a monster party for Christmas—a sort of grand farewell, and I can't imagine how it's to be paid for.'

A roar of laughter came from one of the larger groups.

'You're a dirty old man, Tom Dillon!' someone shouted.

'I'm sorry you're going,' she said.

'Are you?'

'Yes.'

'But you wouldn't even see me.'

'I think I've changed my mind about that.'

Two men fell on the bar, their arms spreading across it.

'Give us some more of that stuff, Mick, we're parched.'

'Come to London.'

'Let's not talk about that now.'

'All right. You know, one wonders about all this moving . . . country to country, house to house, job to job . . . so little of it seems to be gainful. My grandfather stands and watches us as if we were maniacs.'

His eye had caught two new arrivals.

'Oh, God,' he said. 'Talk of the devil. Here comes our hostess, on the move with Lorrimer. What on earth are we going to say?'

'This blasted country,' said Ann. 'It's smaller than a village.'

At that moment no one else was at the bar.

'Hallo,' said Ann. 'We were just . . .'

'It's all right, my dear,' said Norah, in a tense way, 'I don't blame you. I left it too, you see. My own party! Charlie's own party. I'm having a large brandy, Hugo.'

'All very distressing,' said Hugo. 'I didn't really understand . . .'

'That wasn't why we left,' said Patrick. 'We were enjoying it immensely.'

'That's more than I was. Perhaps you didn't see the worst. The place is a shambles now.'

'I'm terribly sorry,' said Ann.

'You don't seem to have found much better here,' said Norah, looking on the company. 'I was nearly knocked down in the hall by a gentleman wishing to make contact with his friends.'

'They're horrors,' said Ann.

Norah was studying her. This situation had a human interest which might perhaps take her mind off the party. She had seen the way they were looking at each other when she came in, and understood it perhaps even better than they did themselves. A Protestant. Poor Moira! It was very intriguing.

Hugo was talking.

'. . . and I probably haven't been here long enough to make these distinctions. I know we English are foolish, but we tend to think of Irish people as being all the same . . .'

They reminded her of something, and she suddenly knew what it was. She had first met Charlie at a bar, in the Marine Hotel, Dun Laoghaire, not so very far from here, and to others they must have looked rather like this. They went for picnics on the Sugarloaf. She thought she had never met anyone so wonderful, and she had been getting worried too, because her juniors, like Moira, had already been married for several years. Once they swam by moonlight, at Killiney. The strange thing was, when she thought about it fairly, without prejudice, he had not really altered much. But for some reason in those days it all seemed to have been happiness and delight.

'You two are looking very glum,' she said, when Hugo had finished. 'The party, I suppose?'

'No, no,' said Patrick. 'We honestly enjoyed it enormously.'

'Young people are so solemn and serious nowadays, aren't they, Hugo?'

'I couldn't agree with you more, my dear. I don't know what's happened to the world. We used to be light-hearted. Indeed, we still are at times, eh?'

He put his hand on Norah's shoulder and shook her a little, which she found slightly irritating. A new thirst seemed to be taking hold of the wedding guests because a dozen or so people had closed in around them at the bar. One of them was singing:

'Patrick McGinty, an Irishman of note,
Came into a fortune and bought himself a goat.'

Norah shuddered.

'Sez he: "Now of goat's milk I'm goin' to have me fill."
But when he brought the nanny home he found it was a bill.'

There were shrieks.

'They're just off the bog, you know,' she said, quite loudly. The brandy was mixing well with the champagne and she felt better. 'It'll take a hundred years for our blessed Republic to become civilised. Crude, ill-mannered, ill-bred louts.'

'Now my dear . . .' said Hugo. He had a confusing memory of Norah vigorously opposing the same statement from Grania, in his dressing-room.

'Your play stands for loutishness too, Hugo. Oh yes, it does. I'm all for loving and living,' she said, looking at Ann and Patrick, 'but not loutishness. However, people want to applaud it, read about it . . . So.' She gestured expansively with her hands.

'There are still a few people who don't,' said Hugo, with some decisiveness. 'I've never been a spokesman for the play, as you well know.'

She knew suddenly what was wrong. It was his affected, pedantic, English voice. She could not endure it much longer. She thought of Charlie's and how there was something warm and natural by comparison.

'I'll have another brandy,' she said. 'A large one.'

Patrick bought it.

'However,' said Hugo, 'I'll admit that brutishness and alcoholism have perhaps never been so much admired. I read somewhere that fatal assaults on women—so popular now—in fact constitute a heroic, if negative, protest against the mediocrity of the times.'

Patrick rather liked Lorrimer. There was something naïve about him, in spite of his portentous appearance, and yet paradoxically he was consciously amusing; which was the only way to be amusing.

'I've noticed with pleasure here,' he said, 'that the theft of £250 from a tobacconist's shop is regarded as a serious headline crime.'

'Quite,' said Lorrimer.

'There are other crimes,' said Ann.

'Quite,' said Norah.

She downed her drink, and was feeling terrific.

'I hate it here,' she said. 'Come on, let's all drive down to the front. A marvellous idea, come on, come on. Let's all look out across the water and make believe we're in France.'

'In France?' said Patrick.

'Where else? Come on. I want to stand in the rain and listen to the sea.'

'All right,' said Ann. 'Why not?'

In the hall a man barged straight through them, shouting 'Paddy!'

'Lout!' said Norah.

Hugo's hired Austin A-40 was at the door.

'We'll follow,' said Patrick.

'No, no,' said Norah, oppressed by the thought of Hugo. 'You two get in the back, come along now.'

They did so. She was not to be denied. She had not behaved like this, or felt so free, in years; not since those old days. She wondered if she had been drinking too much and decided that she had not.

Hugo drove through the town, or village, which laid claim to being Ireland's major coastal resort with a lot of red and yellow paint on the tobacconists, outshining the grey stucco of the upper storeys, and several of the shops modernised in Irish contemporary style. A number still kept the lights on. The rain made it all fresh and gleaming. In most other Irish villages the effects would have been exactly opposite.

'Veronica would have been fascinated by these distinctions,' said Hugo. 'But of course I haven't told you.'

'Told me what?' said Norah distantly.

Patrick was holding Ann's hand in the back, and they were not listening.

'It's evident you don't read our posh Sundays papers, my dear.'

'I haven't had much time today.'

'Well, in both of them, her new novel is extremely well reviewed, and in both—I could scarcely believe it—reference is made to the one indication that the writer is really warm at heart: the charming and affectionate portrait of the actor. Isn't that astonishing, my dear, and such good news?'

'Yes, of course.'

She was not paying attention. She was feeling warm at heart—or somewhere—herself. Vernon would be back in a week, and Andrew. It would make a difference. He had lain on top of her on the Sugarloaf, with the blue sky wheeling above, looking almost the same as he did now. The bamboos could easily be righted and the pistol put back on the wall. To tell the truth, it was due for a bit of a bust-up: it had become a kind of obsession, with every shell in place, and every detail, from the crucifix to the octopus, burning into her brain and absorbing all of her time.

'You don't sound very enthusiastic.' He bent towards her and lowered his voice: 'It doesn't make any difference, of course. I don't even believe it. As I told you, my impression was quite opposite. I'm only pleased on account of the public.'

'Stop here,' she said.

They halted in front of the grey guest-house. She had heard the sea falling on the beach, across the esplanade, below the wall. On

Killiney beach she had knelt and salaamed to the moon and undergone an extraordinary experience. Even Charlie had not known. He was dressing himself, up in the long, spiky grass. This would not be possible now, or perhaps ever again, but she desired intensely to stand on the beach in the rain and look out at the white crests on the dark sea.

She stepped out, slammed the door, and began to run.

'What on earth!' Hugo exclaimed. 'My dear!'

She had gone into the darkness.

He struggled with his own door, muttering: 'This is lunacy. She'll be soaked.'

He began to trot heavily in the same direction. The rain was merciless. Reaching the esplanade he stopped, with his hands on the top of the rails, and looked down. He could see nothing except white foam in the dark.

'Norah!' he roared, in a voice to strike the back of the upper circle. 'Norah! Come back! This is madness!'

There was nothing to be heard, except the sea lapping on the beach.

He began to feel angry and foolish. He supposed it unlikely that she had swum out to sea in the hopes of reaching France. He went back towards the car at a slower trot, opened his door and said:

'Not a sign, not a sign . . .'

The two young people in the back were not aware of him. They were kissing each other, passionately, breathlessly, and even alarmingly.

Hugo stood there, with the door half open, uncertain, with the rain thundering on his balding head and trickling down his neck inside the black alpaca collar of his overcoat.

chapter twenty

Laughter through tears, or sunshine and rain simultaneously, is an Irish phenomenon which perhaps also has its human application. It was the following Saturday and in terms of weather it had been just such a morning. Great black clouds passed across the blue from time to time, and they were still dispensing rain when the sun struck forth again. Their appearance gradually became less frequent, and when the party planners had lunched early, because the Major was going to Leopardstown races, and returned to the sitting-room, the sun was pouring uninterruptedly through the windows.

Nevertheless, it was cold, and they were having their coffee in front of an enormous fire.

Martin, in his unchanging and probably unwashable blue jersey, was talking about malice, which he deemed the supreme characteristic of Dublin and its citizenry. He was reporting all that he had heard spoken about the alleged liaison between Dermot and Hilda.

Dermot, on the sofa, in a red shirt open to the chest, showing black hairs, and a red velveteen coat, much stained with paint, was almost asleep.

Hilda was not, and Grania was worried about her.

Grania had been worried for the past fortnight. Hilda had adopted a brown Irish handwoven garment like a sack, around which she wore a crios, or brightly coloured Irish handwoven belt. Her hair was cut short and in a fringe, in the bohemian style of the early years of the century. She had locked away her jewellery and cultivated an imitation Irish accent which she produced without warning, and without due caution considering that the word 'begorrah' was part of it. Lately she had been discussing the possibility of taking lessons on the harp, and even learning what she called 'Erse.'

About malice she was totally and dangerously uninformed.

'Martin, me bhoy, I think you do be after exaggerating,' she said, lifting her coffee cup with the little finger curled.

'Do you know your present name throughout this friendly city?' Martin demanded.

'Do I have a name? How heavenly.'

'You're known as the Whore of Babylon.'

Dermot guffawed.

'It's not very funny,' said Grania.

Hilda was pale.

'But that's perfectly beastly. I don't understand . . .'

'It's bloody unkind, me ould duck,' said Dermot, 'considering we haven't even done it yet.'

Hilda flushed, and looked pleased, to Grania's surprise.

'Begorrah, it's a shockin' man you're after being,' she said.

'Let's get back to the party,' said Grania. She was wearing a restrained combination of black trousers and a dark green shirt. She felt restrained, having drunk champagne until four that morning in an unsuccessful attempt to persuade Hilda to be more circumspect. 'I've been the subject of this city's malice for a great many years and it bores me stiff. You two were portrait painting and you didn't really hear how we planned the invitations, did they, Martin?'

Martin nodded.

'Everyone is to come dressed as the particular individual they believe themselves to be,' said Grania, with pride.

'Ho, ho, that'll set you a problem, Hilda, me dear.'

'How unkind!' Hilda exclaimed, 'I thought this was me, and you liked it.'

'Oh I love it, me darlin', I love it.'

'Now listen, this is serious,' said Grania. 'Of course you can come as you are, if you are one of the rare ones. But so few have the courage to present themselves as they really, individually are.

We've heard quite enough about malice, parochialism and all the rest of it. This is my statement of the essential value of this country. It looks like being my last. Father has the house in all the papers now and my alimony has become an overdraft.'

'Oh my dear,' said Hilda, 'it's too sad.'

'We know that everyone has two legs and a head and a heart. I want them to show what else they have.'

'That doesn't require fancy dress,' said Dermot. 'I'll show you any time you like, me dark Rosaleen.'

'Oh shut up,' said Martin.

'I'm afraid it'll test my English friends. They've forgotten what it means. Our Sunday reviewers—who are coming by the way—seemed to have joined the general grayness and become just like everyone else on the English scene over the past ten years. They're dear sweet men and I adore them, but I can't tell one from the other any more.'

'Well, let me advise you about one essential addition,' said Dermot, 'even in this land of egos.'

'What's that?'

'Drink, me dear. Drink.'

'Flanagan's ordered forty cases of Heidsieck,' said Grania.

'You're always on about drink,' said Martin.

'And why not? It's in accord with madam's philosophy, isn't it, and the national character? You want people to be more than they will permit themselves. What will achieve that? Drink. It always has. That's why your Irish individuals like it, and bloody good luck to them. You meet a dear old friend in the street. Oh delightful. Oh bloody marvellous. But you are both filled with a total knowledge of the two legs and a head. So what do you both say, to make the encounter more interesting, and even endurable? You said: "What about a drink?" or in this lively land: "What about a jar?"'

'There'll be drink,' said Grania.

She was pleased. Dermot had a surprising way of understanding her.

Finola came in to take away the coffee-tray.

Before doing so, she stood still and murmured: 'I've something to ask you, ma'am. In private.'

'Oh child, must you? You've already told me. You're going to England with whatsisname, and young Trench. It's very regrettable, but we probably couldn't have afforded any of you any longer, so . . .'

'It's not that,' said Finola.

'Well, tell me, child. These are my friends. It won't be published.'

'Well, you see. Mr Trench is getting married . . .'

'Good God.'

'To my sister Kathleen—up at the Neelans. Well, she'll only be moving down the hill, and Father and Mother want to come up and see for themselves, and Father Hanna wants to do it. And so they were goin' to have it here in the village.'

'I see. . . .'

'Well now,' said Finola, gaining confidence, 'the Neelans are in a desperate state on account of what's happened, and won't hear of no parties or receptions or the like. And Mr Trench wondered if they could have it here.'

'Here?'

'Well, that's to say Mr Flanagan says there'd be plenty of space up in his rooms, and he'd be quite agreeable.'

'I see. But when . . . ?'

'It's in three weeks' time when the banns are done. The twenty-second. In the afternoon.'

'But, heavens above, that's the day of my party. Oh, I'm afraid that's quite out of the question.'

'It's only in the afternoon.'

'It seems to me,' said Dermot, 'that it would further your aims. I see great possibilities.'

'Yes,' said Finola enthusiastically. 'We're going to have traditional fiddling.'

'Oh darling, how marvellous,' said Hilda. 'Do let them.'

'I see what you mean, Dermot. All right, Finola, let's have it.'

'Oh gracious, Mr Trench will be delighted.'

Finola collected the coffee-tray.

'As a matter of fact,' said Grania, 'I'd like to do that unfortunate Moira Neelan a good turn. And now she's losing her maid . . .'

'Oh that's all right, ma'am,' said Finola, departing. 'She'll have my sister, Deirdre. She was to be a nun, but it seems there'll be a delay. Father Hanna hadn't met her.'

'This family is inexhaustible,' said Grania. 'Trench marrying again. Well, well.'

'There's life in the old dog yet,' said Dermot.

'Someone talking about me?'

The Major had entered. He spoke gloomily. He paid no attention to the company, but began cleaning his pipe on top of the chest-of-drawers where he kept his pipe-cleaners. He looked very sporty in a short fawn-coloured overcoat and a brown check cap, with race-glasses slung over one shoulder and badges dangling from the leather case. Under his arm he carried the morning paper, folded at the racing page, and when he had cleaned his pipe he sat down, at a distance from the others, filling it from his pouch and marking his newspaper with a pencil.

The others were quiet. Hilda had learned to speak seldom in his presence, and Dermot and Martin were not sure of how they were regarded. Dermot was even unsure about being found sprawled out on the sofa, although not sufficiently so to alter his position.

Grania was ready to talk, although apprehensive. Patrick had broken the news that he was returning to London, and the Major had as yet made no reference to it.

'We've been discussing the party, Father,' she said.

The Major went on reading, but said eventually through his pipe: 'It will ruin us. You know that, of course.'

'Oh Father, it's only the champagne and the band. The plane is free. Sir Harold agreed that the publicity for the company will be worth it. The English papers are sending all their Horse Show reporters and he's giving them the trip on condition they write about it.'

'You might have them add that this house is for sale.'

'That's perfectly possible.'

'It will be sold by then, please God, on paper at least. I've already lost that hovel by the sea. Somebody bought it yesterday.'

'I'm glad. You can't just take *anything*, Father.'

'No?'

'There's another point. Trench is marrying again. Finola's sister . . .'

'Good God.'

'So there'll have to be a place for them both, wherever you go. I've agreed they can have their wedding party in Flanagan's rooms. It's in the afternoon, before mine.'

The Major continued to study form and mark horses without raising his eyes.

'I think you must have suffered some kind of mental relapse,' he said. 'However, I am proposing to enjoy myself today, and am not much interested. Is no one coming with me? Where's Patrick?'

'He's out with Ann Neelan again. I really think it's time we did something about that, Father. Of course, Patrick can't possibly be serious, but even so the Neelans have been quite sufficiently troubled. There's been absolutely nothing else in the papers for the whole week. I see that stinking builder has turned up in Brussels, using another name; not that they can do anything about him. I suppose Neelan is ruined?'

'It seems not. I wrote him my condolences and received a quite remarkable letter this morning. He proposes to erect some kind of museum, holding the records of every ambush of forty years and more ago; examination and admission fees to be paid; a kind of novelist-and-playwright's compendium, with special rates for television authors. He calls it "Memory House", or, less seriously, "Troubles Galore". Apparently "Teeth" Murphy has promised him a considerable sum from the Arts Council, and, even more astonishing, Charlie Gerraty is to be the architect, because "Teeth" will have no other.'

'He's certainly resilient, our Mr Neelan,' said Grania.

'Yes. Our newly-born middle class is undoubtedly full of energy, however misapplied. Patrick came and told me last night that he's going back to London with you. . . .'

'Yes, Father. I'm sorry.'

'Oh that's all right. I was merely going to add that it should mean the end of it, unless of course Miss Neelan is also crossing the water. Everyone else seems to be. I was surprised about that Paddy. I thought he liked the land. I thought he was one of the rare ones. Finola, Mick Trench and Liverpool are not an alternative that would have appealed to me.'

'He's rather good-looking. I suppose that brings temptations. Perhaps he's in love.'

'Ah, it's only the farmyard. Well, I'd better go and make some money to set against this criminal party.'

'It's not just a party, Father,' she said, tossing her head. 'It's an Idea, and one that I would have thought was in accord with your own beliefs, our feeling for the individual. I thought you would approve.'

'I don't understand why it has to be established in my house with a lorry-load of champagne, that's all. The thesis is already proved as far as I'm concerned. Why it's not so for you, I cannot conceive.'

He went out and closed the door quietly behind him. A moment later they heard the car driving away.

Grania was gazing into the fire.

She suddenly knew the answer to his question.

The party was an attempt to persuade herself and the world that her view, and her rôle of patroness and observer, was her sole preoccupation. The doubt had been with her all day—and perhaps all week—although she had been refusing to acknowledge it. These people falling in love, marrying, leaving the coun-

try, had given her a painful feeling which until now she had not
dared to examine. But the truth was that she was weary of this
Man's country, of the juggling and the games, and particularly
of her own detachment and the emotional emptiness she had deliberately chosen here. On first returning she had felt young and
innocent again. She wanted it no longer. She was not consoled,
or cured, after all. She envied these people. She wanted to share
their apparently simple emotions. She wanted to lose herself, as
a woman, like these domestics. She longed for André. Privately,
she denied all that she had said to the contrary on that afternoon
with these people who still surrounded her, who were still talking of a party that she did not want and could not evade, and one
which she was arranging out of a perversity that was now suddenly plain to her. Perhaps her attitude was right—it *was* right in
this all-the-same world—but she was weary of attitudes. Her
father's ideas were *him,* and he needed no proofs, and could
weed his lawn while there was still Edenmore. But it was not so
with her.

'You're looking quite pale, my dear,' said Hilda. 'Has he upset
you?'

'No, no. . . . About the band. There's obviously no hope whatever of getting Tommy Kinsman three days before Christmas,
but Finola has recommended to me some combination—as I think
she calls it—named Jimmy Griffin and his Four Aces. I suppose
that will do.'

'It sounds heaven,' said Hilda.

'This time I shall have to ask for the co-operation of the police.
As soon as Dublin gets wind of it there'll be an army of the uninvited on the way out here. At my last Horse Show dance at
least half the company arrived through the window of the servants' lavatory.'

Heedless of these prospects, the Major was driving across the
hills in a state of illogical contentment. The day was bright and
invigorating. In the distance the Bay was a vivid blue, with one

large white ship moving in towards the river and the great bulk of Howth basking in the sun. Even the wretched Neelan houses in the foreground looked red, glowing and almost agreeable. The first advantage of what people called provincial life was that it was surrounded by readily available beauty. Life anywhere held few other advantages, and he had always been extremely doubtful whether the metropolitans were enjoying any alternative experience, save that of urban putrefaction.

The London plane was now droning overhead, glinting silver against the blue, rising higher on its eighty-minute voyage to the great cesspool. Down below the city spread the tentacles of its red building schemes out across the Central Plain, over which moved a magnificent black cloud, with a suggestion of snow rather than rain. One of the joys of viewing Dublin from up here was that one could forget the quantity of villainy it contained: the tyre-slashers, jerry-builders, horse copers, solicitors on the make, politicians without a conscience, the watchers and waiters to reduce you with pious malice and malicious piety, at the first chink in the armour, to beggary, ruin and exile; and the other and most prevalent form of knavery implicit in the voice on the telephone that said: 'Is that you, Paddy? Well, listen to me, Paddy. I expect you'll remember that good turn I did you a while back. Well, there's this cousin of the wife's, and he's putting in an application for . . .'

Flaming yellow gorse now rose above the stone walls at either side. The Major found it quite splendid here, though at home exterminating it was his main alternative to weeding. What the devil was Grania doing, sitting about with her entourage of three, while the Irish days drifted past? Her ideas were all right, but women had no business with ideas. He supposed she was correct that he should not take just any house. Houses were interesting, as extensions of people; which were the only interesting things about people. He had been moved by the Neelans' plight. But he had also been moved when Trench caught a rat in a wire cage, and had requested him to release the creature at once in the back field. What was moving was the sight of people in their common nakedness. What was interesting was something else. Of course, half the world was starving and suffering. But where economics did make it possible he disliked common denominators and preferred to see people clothed in their own characters; without, however, being prepared to expend forty cases of champagne on the experience. Here it was still possible, but soon the characters would all be tourist touts. 'D'you want a motorboat to the island, sorr?'

His reflection had brought him into a traffic impasse outside the high stone walls and gateway to Leopardstown. The cars from town had met the cars from the country. There was a congestion of muddy, antiquated American sedans, bulging with rubicund gentlemen, behind the thick grey breath on the windows.

Slowly the cars went in line up the driveway. To the left the fields sloped away to the white rails of the course; a sight that always gave him a thrill. At the far window a woman in a black shawl and white apron, of gipsy-like and filthy aspect, was bawling: 'Luvely apples and aaaranges!' and at the driving window a ragged man whose face he knew well roared: 'Race caaaard! Race caaaard!' He thrust them through the window, but the Major shook his head because he had his own follower in the car park.

This gentleman came hurrying through the lines of cars as the Major stepped out on to the ground made soft and muddy by the recent rains. 'Race caaard! Race caaard!' he was roaring. Large patches were missing from his brown coat. One of his lower eyelids had dropped and looked red and sore. He interrupted himself with: 'Afthernoon, Major,' giving a salute, and extracting the top race card from the others by spitting on his thumb. While the Major paid he lowered his voice and murmured out of a corner of his mouth: 'Ballydun in the last race.'

'Do you really think so?'

'A certainty, Major. Practically had it from the bloody horse himself.'

'I'll remember that.'

'A dead snip, Major, a dead snip. Race caaaard . . .!'

Everyone was hurrying up to the turnstiles; men flushed either with health or liquor, in heavy brown belted overcoats; and the 'county', in coats that he sold in his shop and suede furlined bootees, getting out of Jaguars from Meath and Kildare. This was real. This was the country's only passion; eager glinting eyes everywhere, and a rush to get inside.

The horses for the first race were already parading in the paddock; lovely glossy elegant creatures going round and round in that familiar, expectant silence among the observers leaning on the rail, nearly half of whom he recognised.

He remembered that he was supposed to meet the trainer's wife in the bar. She might really have a winner for him. Besides, now that he was here he felt rather skittish. He dreaded setting out for these events alone, but, once arrived, was relieved to be unencumbered by the family, who cramped his style and were only too apt to expose anything he might say as a total fabrication.

The people he had recognised in the paddock were from Dublin. Walking to the bar he passed some more of the 'county', of well-to-do and mildly eccentric appearance. It was perhaps a pity that he recognised so few of them. One heard stories of a decidedly individual form of existence, uninfected by the herd and its views of economic and secure living. Not just champagne and brandy. Who was the man recently, in some passionate conflict over the plain and ageing lady Master of Foxhounds, who had winged his fellow huntsman and competitor with a .22 rifle from the roof of his Victorian castle? He could not remember.

No, the revolting truth was that they were suburbanites, like ninety per cent of the decaying West; yes, even at Edenmore. The rapidly advancing city, brought by Neelan to the very doors, had touched them with its ghastly infection. Grania had asked some 'county' people to the dance: it was one slight reason for looking forward to it.

The woman was at the bar, wearing the coat from his shop, and also her husband, the trainer, who evidently had nothing running in the first race. He was a giant with a face like a beet-root and the Major could see no connection between them, except possibly a talent for living to the full. But even more curious, their daughter Maeve was present, and she was tall, thin, white as a cauliflower, and had clearly not lived at all. This was, of course, one of the dangers for the 'county'; that its essential quality was inclined to meet up, early on, with an English education. So it turned out. Maeve had just been 'finished' in both England and Switzerland, the latter of which was 'such fun'.

'I suppose she has a score of victims notched up here already,' said the Major gloomily. 'It's a most unfair advantage over innocent Irish manhood.'

The parents were delighted; and Maeve too. It was revolting how easily he could make people laugh with this kind of stuff, but pleasurable on the occasion. At the same time he was ever on the look-out for a more rewarding audience, and in the crowded bar he had noticed a remarkable-looking character standing quite near him. This man was apparently listening, although involved with a group of his own, whom he addressed occasionally in a voice of thunder and a foreign accent. He was easy to notice because he had a white and plentiful head of hair, contrasting with a face that was sunburnt dark brown. He was as large as the farmer, but unlike him was exceedingly elegant.

'Well, which of your nags am I to lose my customary half-crown on?'

The wife lowered her voice. 'Make it a bit more than that. Paddy's Purse in the last race.' The husband nodded.

'The last time I saw that animal out it had a heavy limp.'

'Oh, you're a devil. He won't be limping today, believe you me.'

'Besides, my friend in the car park, who must surely be right *some day,* has given me Ballydun.'

'Oh, God help you! Well, *we* can do no more. We'd better be going. We'll see you before then anyhow.'

Everyone was leaving. At the doorway there was a peculiar incident. The Major and the stranger were both standing aside for Maeve. As she went out, the stranger looked at him as if they had known each other for years, smiled, and said softly, and with mockery: 'Your Irish thoroughbreds.'

The Major was too surprised to reply. The stranger departed with his own group, and the Major's companions went away to place bets. He decided to refrain, and was soon up on high, alone, on the stand.

From here the scene was marvellous. It gave him an exhilarating sense of freedom; of sky and air. The day and the sport were a blessed release from confined spaces, from drawing-rooms containing large fires, closed windows and the relentless opinionated cackle of human beings. When life was occasionally good, it was very good. He would not wish to pass away this afternoon. One heard very little about happiness these days, and yet, looking at the swarming crowd below, he thought that there must be a great deal of it about. There were roars of 'Three to one, bar one!' and 'Five to four the field!' There were a number of attractive young women walking about, which was to the good, since beautiful women were in appalling scarcity in the Dublin mountains and he was in considerable need of casting an eye on them from time to time. But the landscape was no less alluring: the great expanse of deep Irish green, spreading away to the bright white rails on the far side, where people were streaming over the course from Foxrock, although the station there was closed and the little branch line from town, having outlived its ancient uses, was now an abandoned trench. Among the trees, the smoke of Foxrock chimneys ascended, directly, but there must have been a wind higher up, because the great black clouds were moving rapidly across the blue. Did any country ever have such clouds? Most effective of all, away to the right, beyond where the horses were coming out, was the gentle line of the Dublin and Wicklow hills, rolling away towards the Sugarloaf.

Norah Gerraty was standing beside him, talking, and her husband was at her elbow, examining the bookies' blackboards through his race-glasses. She was recalling how they had once lived in a dreary place at Foxrock and had been very thankful to move. The Major would have preferred to have been spared the information. She seemed to be in a state of almost hysterical good cheer, and when Charlie lowered his binoculars, the Major was surprised and embarrassed to note how they looked at each other, and laughed together, and called each other 'dear' and 'darling' as if they had only just been married.

'You were a terrible fellow, driving the priest out like that!' she said, and they both laughed loudly.

For the second time that afternoon, the Major was taken off guard.

'I don't mind disappointing scoundrels like you,' he said, 'but I was sorry about that unfortunate Neelan, whose proposition I had greatly preferred. I gather he's forgiven you your deception.'

'Ah, yes, of course,' said Charlie. 'Sure we couldn't live together in this town if we had a memory.'

'I doubt if *she's* forgiven you, dear,' said Norah.

'You're building us a museum, I gather?'

'Oh God, is he still on about that?' said Charlie. 'No, no. That's one of his scatterbrained notions. Himself and "Teeth" Murphy. No, we're on to something much better—Dublin's first multi-storied garage.'

'In combination?'

'Yes. Ah, I was damn sorry for the poor fellow, don't you know. He has a lot of "go" in him, if he'd apply it more wisely. I've got the official contacts that'll make it an economic enterprise and not his usual nonsense, if they'll have him. Of course he wants it to cover Stephen's Green! Whereas it's going to be off O'Connell Street.'

'It's very good news, anyhow.'

The horses were near the start. He was not anxious for conversation. Norah was telling him how marvellous it was that the boys were back for the Christmas holidays: Andrew was out golfing, his new game; and Vernon was painting the garage pink. She thought she'd give herself an outing for once. She hadn't been racing for ages, and she couldn't think what had come over her to be missing all this.

He was not listening. His eyes had fallen on one figure, moving through the crowd below with a springy step and talking, it seemed, to everybody. It was the stranger again. He looked as if he had just left the Ritz Bar and turned up at Longchamps. He wore a black suit with a very strong white stripe, double-breasted and of immaculate cut, carefully moulded around shoulders that might have belonged to a bull. It was set off by a white carnation.

'Do you know who that man is, down there, with the white hair?'

'Where? Oh yes,' said Norah. 'We were wondering about that that too. He's most definitely not Irish. He's not one of the usual crowd. The funny thing is, we both thought we'd seen him somewhere before, but for the life of us we couldn't think where.'

'They're off!'

The Major found himself watching both the race, on which he had wagered nothing, and the object of their remarks, who had come to rest among some of the native troglodytes. The Plain People of Ireland. He wondered which of the ruling agencies had invented that expression, and wherein lay its glory, being solely interested himself in the un-Plain People of Ireland. The stranger in fact stood closest to 'Twitcher' Doyle, the district justice who had recently produced the most acid ban yet formulated on dancing after midnight, and promptly raised emigration for the district in question by several hundred people.

The Major experienced a curious combination of national and

personal pride. He suddenly wanted to talk to this cosmopolitan, to this fresh face after all these years, and show him that in this country the Yahoos had not yet entirely taken over.

It looked as if he would not have the opportunity. Race followed race, and he did not see the newcomer again. He was three pounds down, which was about average. The last race was approaching. He put an unaccustomed tenner to win on Paddy's Purse, which was quoted at ten to one, ignored Ballydun, the favourite, and went to the bar for a 'stiffener'. There was a certain amount of liquid on the floor by now and a few broken glasses, and more thirsty people were present than at any time previously. Nevertheless, out of the bedlam one voice, and person, appeared very distinctly beside him.

'You understand these haarses?'

It was a strong face, with a formidable chin and what looked like a sabre cut on one cheek. At the same time there was something friendly, simple and even boyish about it, and the eyes seemed to be laughing. He was nearly a foot taller than the Major.

'Horses? Well, I *used* to . . .'

'I too! I used to understand haarses, but *these*? My Gott!'

He struck the bar with his fist; the bottles and glasses at one end jumped and clashed together, and a barman shouted: 'Hey, steady on, Tarzan!'

This went unheard.

'Natchur-a-lee they are Irish haarses. So!'

'So they are quixotic.'

'Eggsactlee.'

He said this very quickly and decisively, and with a look of approval at the Major.

'Like the people. That is why I am here. They are the only people like the Poles. A drink. Kum, kum!'

He hit the bar more lightly. The barman came, looking surprised and grim, but making no retort.

'Two large ones. You know Sir John Cromarty?'

'No.'

'He is quite crazy. You don't know him? My God.'

'I'll be on my ear if I drink this. I'm an old man.'

'Naturally.'

'What did you say?'

The Major was shocked, amused and intrigued, in turn.

'I have seen you somewhere. I knew it at once. A very long time ago when I was a boy, so you must be old, naturally. Ha, ha!' He emitted a sudden crackling roar. 'Don't worry.' He placed a hand on the Major who thought for a moment that his shoulder-blade had been snapped in two.

'You're Polish?' he said, when he could speak.

'Ye-es. I am a count.'

'Really? I am a major.'

'Ha, ha! I am also, but in peace-time a count. Let us drink to it.'

'And what are you doing among us provincials?'

'Ho, ho. Is that what you say?'

'Aren't we obviously so?'

'Not at all! I don't understand. I'm not an intellectual, you know. Please!'

'What made you think I was?'

'Something about you, my little one.'

'Did you call me your "little one" or has the whisky gone to my ears?'

'Well, you're not big, are you? My God. No, no, I am sorry.'

The Count put out a hand, more gently.

'That's quite all right.'

'No, no, this was rude.'

'Take your hand away,' said the Major, brushing it aside amusedly with his glass. 'These foreign courtesies alarm us. We don't go in for manners in this country.'

'Look here,' he added, suddenly remembering where he was and noting that the last few people were downing their drinks and leaving. 'This is absurd. The last race will be starting.'

'So what! You don't ride, do you? Don't be silly. Be calm.'

'I *did* ride. That might have been when you saw me.'

The Count was suddenly excited.

'What is your name? Kum. Quickly!'

'Murrough-Bryant.'

'My God!'

'That seems excessive. Excuse me, I've got to see this race.'

The Major turned and walked towards the door. He felt something underneath both armpits, and then was in the air, whirling in a circular motion. He landed hard on a chair and bounced. The room spun and settled. The barman was gazing at him in mute astonishment. The Count was beside him, saying more calmly: 'But this is quite extraordinary.'

'That's an understatement.'

The Major gave his head a shake.

'Two large whiskies, please. Yes, yes. It was Amsterdam, 1926. Yes?'

'Are you aware that you have just thrown another human being across a public bar—a gentleman of advanced years, with a reputation to maintain in these parts?'

'Oh, shush, shush, shush. Amsterdam, yes? Kum, kum.'

'It's possible. I don't see that it's so extraordinary, except that it ages *you* somewhat. I may never recover from this. I think you've fractured my posterior.'

'Here. Drink, drink. This *is* extraordinary.'

'I wish you'd stop saying that.'

'Naturally.'

'And that. I've got a large sum of money on this race.'

'Pooh. I've lost two hundred and fifty. No more horses today, please!'

'You mean you've lost that this afternoon?'

The Major was impressed.

'Naturally. Yes, it was Amsterdam. And you were *magnificent*.'

'Are you serious? Just say "yes", not the other thing.'

'Ye-es.'

The Major looked about him. It was all slightly out of focus. He drank his whisky.

'There's not many people who remember.'

He was touched.

'Exactly.'

'Why were you there?'

'I was riding. *You* don't remember *me*. Why should you? I was a child.'

'Why don't you sit down? You alarm me.'

'I don't sit. The Germans made me sit for two years.'

'I don't think I'll ever stand again after my more recent experience.'

'Yes, you and Sugar Sweet. *There* was a horse!'

'That's true. That's true. What are you doing here?'

'Buying a farm and house. I am a very good farmer. This will surprise you, eh? And I like these crazy people. I was here before, many years ago. This time I have only been here a week and I like them again.'

'They must be "county" people.'

'Not necessarily. You are too close perhaps, eh? You should travel.'

'God forbid.'

'This interests me. I see you are a man of theories, my little one. I prefer actions. So now we are going. Kum.'

'Going? Going where?'

'To my house. It's only three miles away. I have rented it from Sir John Cromarty. You shall see how I cook. You shall dine like a king.'

'I'm not interested in food.'

'What? Oh, you poor man, you are scarcely alive, you know that? Kum. I will show you.'

'I have no intention of going.'

'You have a car? I came in Lady MacDermot's. But they won't miss me, those people.'

'I have. But another time, perhaps. Not now.'

'This is wrong!'

The Count had grasped an empty Guinness bottle and thumped it on the counter.

'It must be now. Always. You must live as if you are about to die. This is the unfortunate aspect of Lady MacDermot and her party of blackguards. They think they will never die. Then poof! It's over. They have done nothing. They know nothing. Naturally.'

'I see you have your theories too. Curiously enough I share this one. I've always lived as if I was about to die, which has now become only too likely. But in my case it has never meant tearing about the place.'

'Ha, ha, ha! Bravo. But let's do it my way this time, eh? You can drive very, very slowly if you wish.'

'I'd certainly need to in this condition.'

'Kum. Kum.'

The Count moved towards the door, with a commanding motion of his head.

'Come, come, yourself!' said the Major.

But he was rising. The move was not as painful as he had anticipated. Yet outside he found that he was walking in an uncertain manner. It was confusing: a great number of people walked with them. The last race must be over. He had forgotten about it.

'How many of those drinks have you had, as a matter of interest?'

'Oh, a dozen or so. It was those bloody horses. But it does not touch me.'

'You're fortunate. It's freezing hard all of a sudden. I don't know how you exist without a coat. I think it's going to snow.'

'It's only your condition, little one. Kum.'

The Count was marching ahead.

The race-card seller had converted himself into a car-park attendant. He received the Major with a woebegone expression, his red eyelid drooping wretchedly.

'My God, that was a shock for us, eh, Major? I couldn't be more mortified, honest to God, Major. Paddy's Purse. I never even heard of the bloody horse.'

'It won?'

'It did indeed. I suppose you weren't even lookin' with that bloody Ballydun way down the course. Well, better luck next time, eh?'

'Yes.'

'What's this?' asked the Count, striking the bonnet of the Vauxhall. 'It's no two-year-old.'

'Be careful. I think the insurance may have elapsed.'

Inside, searching for his keys, with the Count seeming enormous beside him, the Major said: 'I've just won a hundred pounds.'

He was glowing. He had never had such a success at a meeting in his life.

'You rotten blackguard. Why didn't you tell me?'

'We've only just met. Remember?'

'Back away! Back away!' shouted the tipster.

They followed the line of cars down to the main gate. It was growing dark. The Major shivered. The glow was merely internal.

'My God, it's cold.'

'Pah, you should go to Warsaw. That can be cold.'

'I don't want to, thank you.'

'Though never too cold for killing Germans. My God!'

'Really?'

'Some of us Poles did not give in, you know.'

The Major glanced at his alarming companion and saw that he was watching the road apprehensively.

'It must have been hell.'

'No! You silly fellow. Fighting is living. They caught me, the blackguards. Two years in prison. My silly hair turned white, God knows why. They thought I would be more use alive. So I escaped, through Yugoslavia. North Africa. Italy. France.

I've kept my boots. I wore them all the way. Under the Arc de Triomphe. I was proud.'

'Understandably. You're not making this up?'

'No, you naughty fellow, there are some things that are not funny, even from Irishmen. I've also kept the Croix de Guerre and the Légion d'Honneur. You may see them. Turn right and go through Foxrock.'

'I'm sorry. We've been neutral and out of touch with the world's ways for so long, you know. It's in the distant past, but I never had quite the same feeling about my war; only nightmares. I still have them.'

'You must have been young.'

'Very.'

'That was good. Young people must have wars. It is part of life, quite simply. And after, you are not so young, and silly. I would go back to Warsaw and fight those other blackguards now, but I am getting too old.'

'"Wars are part of life" is the kind of statement which the women in my house would greet with platitudinous catcalls of protest.'

'Naturally.'

'Probably my grandson as well.'

'He's not a soldier?'

'He's been in an advertising agency.'

'Oh, my God. Would he like to go to Warsaw? I have contacts.'

'I doubt it very much. Are you wearing perfume? There's the most obnoxious stink in the car, and it's hard enough for me to drive as it is. Phew!'

The Major cleared his nose.

'I like to be clean.'

'Irish manhood doesn't approve of such cissy habits.'

'Oh, ho, ho!'

The Count roared and shook.

'Irish manhood. That is very, very good! You are a funny one.'

The Major paused at a crossroads, for further directions.

'And what is wrong with these women in your house, eh?'

'The universal fault. No knowledge. Closed minds and opinions culled at second-hand.'

'We must be foolish to be so often deceived. But *I* gave you an opinion.'

'About wars? Yes, but it was your own. It was, in Keats's phrase, an "axiom" that you yourself had "proved upon your pulses".'

'Ah, Keats, poor blackguard. That silly little Fanny Brawne!'

'You know about Keats?'

'Naturally. Pooh. What do you think I am, eh?'

'I'm beginning to think you're most remarkable.'

'Now don't start being silly. We're just there. In the next gate, please.'

They went up the short drive to a house that the Major found surprisingly pleasant in this newly rich, suburban, stockbrokers' area. It was small, yellow and Georgian.

An ageing butler in a white coat opened the door.

'Major Murrough-Bryant will be staying to dinner. They know what to do.'

'Very well, sorr.'

As he departed the Count said: 'He was dead drunk when I arrived. He is better now. You want to wash?'

The Major washed. There were famous horses on the walls of the bathroom, but the afternoon had been too eventful for him to concentrate on them. He returned to find the Count standing by a collection of bottles in the small sitting-room. He had turned on the lights, and one of them was above the portrait over the mantelpiece: a gentleman in R.A.F. uniform with a wide ginger moustache.

'Sir John. Crazy, but quite charming.'

'That's the sort of person I'd find it difficult even to begin to speak to.'

'Yes, yes, of course. You'd prefer T. S. Eliot. You'll have a drink?'

'I don't . . .'

'Kum. Kum.'

The Count handed him one. The Major sat on the chintz-covered sofa.

'You have seen this?' the Count demanded, with sudden parade-ground ferocity.

An Irish newspaper lay on the arm of the sofa, and he slapped it with the back of his hand.

'What?'

'This snivelling little art critic!'

'You read art criticism?'

'Oh shut up, or I will be angry. This fellow Sleator, I don't know what he does, but he paints. So this sickly little black-guard comes and wipes his nose in it. Art is important, yes?'

'I think it's the only thing that is. Religion is only a lesser form . . .'

'But critics are not. Who is this rotten little parasite? Martin O'Keeffe, who is that? I would spank him, you know. What is it you say, six of the best? It would hurt.'

'I can imagine.'

'Exactly. A moment please. This drink is warm. We must have ice.'

The Count strode across the room, opened the door, raised his hands and clapped them together with a detonation.

Almost instantly, a young blushing maid in cap and apron appeared, whispering: 'Yes, sorr?' with a look of awe almost adoration at the Count.

'Ice, please. At once!'

She vanished.

The Major sat gazing at him.

'That was an Irish servant?'

'Naturally.'

'Were they like this when you came?'

'Certainly not. They were drunk.'

'And you've been here a week. Good God.'

'Exactly.'

The Count allowed himself a show of vanity, grinning.

The maid came rushing to the sideboard with the ice. The Count snapped his fingers together and pointed at the table in front of the sofa. She placed it there and hurried out, nearly tripping at the doorway.

'Well!' said the Major.

'She has fine breasts, eh? Like balloons. But she is a child.'

The Count sat in one of the arm-chairs by the hearth. The Major had only now noticed that the fire burning there was as ferocious as those he so much disliked at home.

'You seem suddenly depressed,' he said. 'For someone as complete as I take you to be, you have the most variable moods.'

'I'll tell you, little one. I took a child away with me, like a fool. She had the brains of a hen. My God! And do you know why I did it? I thought I was still young. Or rather, I wanted to prove it to myself. And left a woman who was worth two hundred of this one. I have known many women, but none like this. I was married once. One has to, at times. Besides I wanted children. Sons—not girls, my God. I had two. I don't remember their names. They went away. Quite rightly. Quite rightly.'

The Count looked gloomy again. The Major was about to remark on it, but restrained himself. He did not think that he had ever been so impressed by another human being before; not, at least, since his youth. This man's extensions were the direct revelation of his inner self. They were him. He was complete; and had become so the only possible way, by learning it on his pulses. When he said 'I', he spoke the truth.

Those asses at home would never understand, though he intended to tell them.

'You know I have only been here seven days. Straight from

Paris. That's why I go racing in these clothes. And already a priest called. We had some drinks. He said I should get married. "Look," I said, "I make a bargain with you. You get married. I get married." '

The Major chuckled.

'What did he do?'

'He went away. The funny thing is, I intend to get married.'

'Really? To the woman you spoke about?'

'Yes, she is in London. She does not know it yet, but this will be all right. We are both restless, you understand. So I am buying the house, and will say: "This is for you. . . ." '

'Yes, I can imagine that. You're just the sort of man who presents flowers. Another sissy and un-Irish habit.'

'Exactly. And I will say: "Here we are and here we stay." '

'In Ireland? Will she stand for it? Are there such women?'

'Yes, there are, little one. You should know. She is your daughter.'

The Major had the same sensation as when he was hurled through the air. After a moment he put down his glass, his hand shaking slightly.

'Which one?'

'Ha, ha, the London one, naturally!'

'Delia! God help you, you idiot.'

'No, no, she is in Paris. I have seen her. She is living with an artist who is dying.'

'What? Oh, this is too much. No one tells me anything these days.'

'No, no, it is Grania, adorable, wonderful Grania. How could *you* have produced such a one?'

'I begin to see. I thought there'd been too many stray counts about lately. I had an intimation earlier on, but it vanished under the heavy strain of the afternoon. Your name is André?'

'Exactly.'

'My grandson mentioned you.'

'Ye-es. I knew he was in advertising. I was teasing you. So

now you see what was so extraordinary. Our meeting! And why I had to be a little rough.'

'A little? I don't know why you bothered with me. She's not in London. She's here.'

'Here? Grania? My God!'

'Certainly. I left her at home a few hours ago, with Dermot Sleator and his best friend, Martin O'Keeffe.'

'My God, what a country,' said the Count in a vague way. 'They eat each other and this is friendship. Oh, but I am a fool. I will have to be quick.'

'A complete fool, in my opinion.'

'Quite rightly. Quite rightly.'

'I mean, she'll drive you mad within a week.'

'Don't be silly, please. You are like her, little one, though you cannot see it, naturally.'

'She is possibly a feminine debasement of myself. I prefer women to be really stupid . . .'

'Yes, yes, of course. You Irishmen never grow up.'

'I mean, stupid enough to be dumb.'

'Ho, ho! That is unfortunately extremely rare. No, no, you come to Paris. I will make a man of you. My God, I will show you women of beauty, wit and intelligence that will make even *you* live again, my little Diogenes!'

'I'm afraid it's too late for that. In any case you are settling down among the crazy people in this godforsaken island, I think I should remind you.'

'Quite rightly. Quite rightly.'

'I'm still not used to it, and doubt if I will be in this life. I'm also a little jealous.'

'Ha, ha. What is this?'

'I was going to present you to them as my example of a complete human being and an answer to the contemporary anæmia.'

'Ah, yes, I know you. You would present your lion, but I would refuse to roar.'

'You are one, nevertheless. You could not be a horse. You are who you are, all through.'

'No, no, a bear is what you want. A performing bear, on a lead. And like a bear I would like to strangle you.'

The Count leaned across and placed a hand around the Major's throat.

The Major turned crimson, spluttered, and said, coughing, 'You nearly have.'

'I am sorry. You are sometimes foolish.'

'Perhaps it's because I'm going senile, or maybe it's the whisky. But I don't think so. It's been a curious afternoon.'

'Ah, ha. But I have forgotten. Now that you know my name, I will show you.'

The Count strode across the room, threw open Sir John's escritoire, and took out a leather folder. He placed it on the Major's lap. It contained a heap of orders, ribbons and citations.

'Now I will leave you, to make the sauce. You will eat as never before.'

'I'll be sick.'

'Oh, you have so much to learn! This is the only way in which this country is provincial, and you too. They drink, like primitive people, but they do not know how to eat. Food and wine are materials for the mind, my friend. Eating is of the spirit. And afterwards we will talk.'

'More talk?'

'Naturally.'

'Oh, my God!'

The Count left the room.

Count André Rodzinsky he was called, the Major discovered, and he had clearly been a man of incredible courage. But he was not reading with great concentration. He was thinking. Quite apart from the hundred pounds, the Fates seemed to have been behaving with extraordinary friendliness all day.

The Count returned.

'Is this all genuine?'

'About some things I do not permit joking, understand?'

He softened.

'The boots are upstairs.'

'You brought them with you?'

'Naturally. But wait. I have been thinking. Where am I to buy a place? Quickly. I have already seen three rotten ruins.'

'I've been thinking too. Could you not forget your continental and rather schoolboyish pride and allow the lady to present the bouquet to you? I thought that was done abroad, in any case.'

'Please?'

'I mean, you wouldn't need to buy anywhere, provided you allowed your father-in-law to retain his room.'

'Ha, ha!'

The Count stood as if shot. Then he began to walk up and down, running a hand through his white hair and murmuring: 'Yes, yes, perhaps, since we are in a hurry. It is quite large, I have heard. And with a farm?'

'Sixty acres. Well?'

The Major was turning his injured neck, from the sofa.

'Yes, yes. A drink! Sometimes you are not so foolish, my little Chocolate Major!'

'Well, Jack, I don't know what to make of your daughters, honest to God I don't.'

Mrs Doyle, in black wedding-dress, coat and hat, her powerful arms folded on her chest, towered over her wizened husband in his bowler beside her. He wore his suit, having been unaware that he was coming to a grand white wedding.

In a third chair, Deirdre, wearing a ragged straw hat with a cherry in it, rolled her eyes dreamily towards the window. Her sister Finola was absent, keeping at a safe distance from the parents.

They waited in Flanagan's sitting-room, upright on the chairs, as if they were going to be called for medical examination at any moment. The afternoon sun, reflecting in from the snow on the courtyard roofs, gave a sordid appearance to the array of bottles on the temporary bar from which Mr O'Toole had agreed to dispense at the reception. The stretcher-bed, on which Deirdre had lately been resident in place of the Neelans' bath, had been joined by two others, on which the Doyle parents would spend the night. All three were for the moment piled in a corner.

'One marrying. One running off to foreign parts with a man. One turned down by the Church.'

'They're lively, all right,' said her husband, giving a toothless chuckle, so that she glanced at him in surprise.

'I'm not turned down, Ma,' said Deirdre, 'I'm to be examined.'

'You'd need it, girl! Sleeping here with that one. Are you out of your wits?'

'I'm not sleeping with him, Ma. He's in next door. He's a funny one. He was that excited this morning he lost his wig!'

Deirdre gave a sudden robust laugh, and both parents looked smartly at her. At once her expression was the same as before, and they wondered if they had heard aright.

'It's lucky for you Martin didn't come up with us. He'd have put an end to Mr Flanagan's fishing for a while!'

Mrs Doyle was referring to the decorative net, covering one wall, which Flanagan had purchased from a young fisherman in Cannes at an exorbitant price. It was now strung with holly and ivy brought in from the garden by the bridegroom, Mr Trench.

'And here I am, forbidden to dress me own daughter, with all the arty ones around her.'

In Flanagan's neighbouring bedroom Kathleen was receiving the final touches of her wedding-gown from its designer, Dan Lavelle. He knelt at her feet, while Richard, who had followed Kathleen down the hill, sniffed around him. He was perfectly happy with this extravagant notion of Grania's, since a full account was going into the Irish Sunday papers, and the costuming of an Irish servant-girl was just the thing likely to take him successfully to New York.

On Flanagan's bed, with its brilliant striped cover, picked up from a young pseudo-Arabian in Nice, Dermot Sleator lay drawing the bride and singing to himself. He thought her quite touching; particularly the detail of her spectacles. She was looking almost pretty. Under Julia Byrne's very eyes she had departed down the hill with the cake-tin of cosmetics, and Dan Lavelle had given her some useful advice.

Grania had conceived of both commissions in order to please the parents. André, who had been through two fortunes but still possessed a third, was prepared to grant her anything. Indeed, he had suggested that the couple should take their honeymoon in Monte Carlo, but they had said that they preferred the gate lodge. She knew that the Doyles would have liked better a sketch by Terence Keogh, but he had been causing frightful disturbances lately of the kind that Dermot had sense enough to reserve for other lands.

'You know, young one,' said Dermot, 'you and me have the qualities this ould country is losing.'

He went on drawing, between reflections.

'A sense of delight . . . a capacity for joy . . . appreciation of the God-given day . . . an *unconquerable* spirit . . .'

'Ah, you should 'a' seen me a while back, Misther Sleator,' said Kathleen, blushing. 'My spirit was nearly conquered then. But I prayed.'

The day, and her important position, had given her an extraordinary confidence among these great men.

'Quite rightly, quite rightly, as our new friend is wont to remark.'

Richard barked, and Dan Lavelle nearly fell over.

Kathleen thought that it was in approbation, but the dog had rushed to the window.

André, Grania and the Major had come into the glittering, snowy courtyard on three hired horses. A dusty American taxi was there, ordered for the wedding guests, and the driver stood stamping his feet beside it.

'Here we shall have the pigs,' said André, dismounting. 'And the cows milked by machinery, and everything modern and clean.'

Richard having, as was his custom, asked for all the doors to be opened, came rushing gleefully out. The Count seized him by the muzzle, saying: 'Hallo, my little one.' The dog fought for breath with his tail between his legs, and on being released ran whimpering away.

'Oh, my God, an Irish dog!' said André. 'In Poland, you know, I used to hunt with ten white Alsatians. They are quite rare. They could take a bear like this. Grrrr! Where is the bride? Is it time? She is in our Celtic treasure's rooms, eh?'

'Yes, up there,' said Grania. 'We must go and change now.'

Just before she dismounted, the Major noted once again how faultlessly she sat in the saddle. She looked so happy, with her Count. Riding was the life!—although the hedgerows which the

Count intended to uproot in the future, had kept them almost to walking pace. He himself was very contented and unusually fit. A few days ago the latter description had not applied. On tasting the Count's *boeuf* Stroganoff, he had decided that he must be a gourmet after all, eaten well, and only a few hours later suffered from crippling indigestion. He wondered if that was why his first attitude towards the Count was so difficult to maintain; or was someone of the calibre he had detected simply too exhausting for a person of his advanced years?

In either case one was reminded of the limiting nature of the physical and of the overriding importance of health, to which poor Keats had made such frequent reference. Thoughts were routed every time by *boeuf* Stroganoff, a lift in the air, a hand around the throat, or a station wagon hurtling through a marquee.

He had lately remembered that incident.

There was to be no Horse Show marquee for this dance, since it was far too cold and the snow was three inches deep on the tennis-lawn. Instead, Patrick and Ann were supervising the adaptation of the long hallway into a ballroom.

A fire was roaring in the great fireplace, warming up the armour of the knight. Near him stood a large, illuminated Christmas tree, and they were placing crackers along the ledge of the oak panelling. Grania, having sensed that her original theory for this party was already crumbling in practice, as theories do, had decided to save it, if need be, in the guise of a Christmas celebration.

Flanagan was absent, in the kitchen basement, instructing a surprised group of hired apprentice waiters in the night's procedure. But Finola was vaguely helping, with interruptions to giggle with Paddy, who was shyly lurking outside the front door.

Eventually they were joined by Mick Trench, looking exceedingly odd in morning clothes, who had arrived to say that Duff, the best man, had assisted his father into his own rented costume and they were preparing, as arranged, to proceed to the church in the front of a friend's lorry.

'Where do Jimmy and the Aces go?' he inquired.

'There on the landing, at the top of the stairs.'

'Looks all right. And we have to put up with that bloody fiddler!'

'Perhaps you can come and look in on us,' said Patrick. 'Mother!' he shouted up the stairs. 'Trench is ready to go to the church. Hurry up!'

'Coming, darling.'

In her room she was changing into a Parisian suit of pale grey. The room was in disarray and her jodhpurs lay on the floor. So did the English papers which Flanagan had brought up in the morning with a half-bottle of Heidsieck. The world outside Ireland was still active. Several hundred millions were to be spent on a new long-range deterrent; 143 Africans and two whites had been killed in self-government clashes; the police were disinterring five bodies in Camberwell. But these were not the reasons why she read the papers. All the best-known columnists carried stories of yesterday's chartered flight of guests. Last night they had been crowding the Shelbourne, Gresham and Hibernian hotels, and some of them had visited Ireland's first night club, where Stavros Caramanos had welcomed them in the Irish language and served them with Gaelic coffee in emerald green goblets.

'Darling, I've been looking for you all day. Where on earth have you been?'

Hilda had appeared, in a brown sack of Irish tweed.

'Riding. Listen, dear, I'm in a terrible hurry . . .'

'But you don't know what's happened! Look, a telegram. From Reggie. "All is over. Coming to the party. Forgive me. Your loving husband. Reggie." '

'That's marvellous, dear. They're all returning, poor children. But we really must rush. Are you coming?'

'Yes, yes. But *is* it marvellous? Can I forgive him?'

'Well, what do you feel?'

'Well, yes. But the point is—will he understand Ireland?'

'Begorrah, why not? Though he may not recognise you at first. Come along now, Hilda.'

Grania hurried ahead down the stairs. She ought to have been delighted, but she was almost afraid now to hear of any more oddities coming to the party. André thought it a perfectly reasonable project. He was all right. He was wearing his uniform and decorations and those simply frightful boots. But God knows what others might find themselves compelled to do. The phone had been ringing for two weeks with half-witted inquiries as to what was meant by 'Fancy Dress—i.e., Come as the person you really fancy yourself to be.' Dermot had lately been enigmatic about his costume, but previously he had threatened to come naked; and there might be others, even in this weather.

Out in the yard, where the snow was disintegrating from the roofs and dripping from the gutters in the sunshine, there was confusion and excitement.

Into the battered American taxi crowded Mrs Doyle, Deirdre, Mick Trench, Mary Cullen, that seldom-seen figure from the kitchen who was already close to tears because she had known Mr Trench for a long time, and Finola, flamboyantly clothed in red and green, with a large green picture hat. Paddy had chosen to go up the hill in the back of the groom's lorry rather than face Mrs Doyle again. There was a moment's delay when Kathleen, suddenly becoming far from calm, cried from the window that Richard, her sole confidant throughout the past months, was to be taken to the church in the car. But this was rejected, and the party went on its way.

The Major followed in the Vauxhall, with Patrick and Ann beside him, and the Count between Grania and Hilda in the back.

Flanagan was to come soon afterwards, with the bride and her father, in the Bentley, which had been moved into the yard so that the garage could accommodate the three horses hired from a riding establishment across the mountains.

The Major had been happy enough, since it was ordained, to disinter his morning clothes and honour Trench and his forty years' loyal service. At the same time he considered that in ordaining this full-dress performance Grania was once again being patronising, without understanding, and he had told her so.

'Which side are *you* on in this marital contest?' he asked Ann.

'Oh, the bride's, of course. She's still with the Neelans, you know, until the words are spoken.'

Patrick was pleased at how well these two had been getting on lately, but not pleased by the Major's remark, because it touched on a subject he wished to avoid.

'Yes, I've been thinking that the late Mrs Trench must be turning furiously in her grave: the unfortunate Trench supported by a car-load of dubious Protestants!'

'Ah, ha!' said André, from the back. 'Who is dubious? I am not dubious.'

'I wouldn't know what you are, to tell the truth.'

Patrick felt like saying: 'You seemed to know all right the other night.' He had been much impressed, and a little mystified by the Major's astonishing return home and his discourse on 'the first real human being', which had ended with the startling announcement to Grania: 'Most incredible of all, he wants to marry *you!*'

The snow was deep under the rhododendrons, although out on the road it was turning to slush. The mountains ahead of them were white. It was rare for Christmas to be so correct.

The taxi had emptied its passengers, who had gone down the walk towards the church and Father Hanna's house, but the Neelans had just arrived in their Jaguar, with the straight-backed figure of Julia Byrne in the rear.

Moira wore the beige hat and veil, and Tom was in morning clothes. All this presumption on the part of their neighbour had not displeased her as much as might have been expected. In the first place, the Murrough-Bryants were so infinitely preferable to the Gerratys: she remembered in what a kindly manner they had received her on that terrible night. In the second place, she was excited about being invited to the dance. She even wondered whether one should be displeased with Ann for forming an alliance—of whatever kind it might prove to be—with a member of the house that seemed, at the moment, to be the cynosure of the entire British press.

A group of villagers and small ragged children watched these grand people meeting, some of them with faces of awe and others with whispered comments that provoked chuckles from their neighbours. Tom, who had for weeks been subject to the traditional stream of anonymous phone-calls, was ready for anything, but the housing estate was evidently not represented among the onlookers. Unmolested, they walked down the path which had been swept clear of snow.

Soon afterwards the Bentley was spotted, driven with slow dignity up the hill by Flanagan. He was not in the least offended at being placed in the service of the Doyles. It reinforced the view of Ireland he had expressed to his mistress that brilliant morning in October: 'Sure *we're* the democrats!'

The spectators were now quiet because the bride, seated with her father in the back, looked truly regal: an impression only slightly spoiled by the fact that when she raised her full skirt to step forth Richard leaped out from under it, where he had been secreted, and danced about in the snow with shouts of joy. He was scarcely noticed. There were gasps at the vision of the bride.

The Major had taken his place at the back of the church, which he was visiting for the first time in his life. The smell of incense made him feel slightly ill, and reminded him of the curious odour the Count had brought into his car. Examining the congregation in front of him, he noted that the Protestant representation, though formidable enough, was not as embarrassing for Trench as might have been expected, since a number of unknown villagers had swelled the company on either side.

When the bride entered, he wondered if Grania was perhaps justified. It was a staggering transformation. Mr Doyle was grinning irreverently, whether with paternal pride or with his curious sense of humour it was hard to determine.

They were then assailed, from the Major's point of view, with a plenitude of tinkling bells, accompanied by motions that he did not attempt to imitate, and an incomprehensible stream of Latin from Father Hanna, until he was called back to attention by the clear voice of Kathleen saying: 'I will.'

'I will,' she repeated, and the priest stumbled a little, but recovered.

Then everyone was seated, except the two participants, while the priest stood on the step above them, looking strangely paternal with his white close-cut head emerging from his white surplice.

'Now then, you two,' he said, in his customary forthright manner. 'You're married in the eyes of God and you're going to stay that way. I want to hear no nonsense about *that*. We've had an example only too recently of the tragedies that follow when homes are insecurely founded. Those were architectural faults —and damnable ones, in my opinion. I, of course, am concerned with moral faults, and those of another creed who are among the company today will know full well what I mean by that!'

Father Hanna crossed his arms and allowed his penetrating blue eyes to gaze out of his ruddy, knobbly face at each of the newcomers among his congregation.

'In the True Faith,' he said, raising his voice, 'there is no divorce! We all know well, do we not, how the followers of other creeds choose to lead their lives? Is it not the present ruin of countries other than our own, thanks be to God? Countries not so far across the water where families are divided, children lack guidance and control, and, as was shamefully depicted in one of our theatres not so long ago, delinquency runs riot. Among such people, husband and wife have a tiff—or something of the sort—some slight quarrel over something or other. And what do they say? They say: "Let's get a divorce." Oh yes. No question of making an effort. No question of the holiness of matrimony. Oh no! They ask for a divorce—and they get it, what's more. *But not with us!'*

The priest paused to let the echo die down, and the Major rose quietly and walked out.

He felt a wave of nausea in the doorway, but the air was crisp and wholesome and he recovered after a moment. Richard came running up, covered in snow, and the Major patted him. He took his pipe from his pocket and wandered down the walk, lighting it. He suddenly smiled to himself at the recollection that the *Ballynoggin Star* had arrived that morning with his article hidden among the obituary notices at the back. The spectators had dispersed from the white road. He stood looking down on Dublin, which was marvellously clear today, and felt an unaccustomed affection for the city. Whether they were attractive like this one, or revolting like most others, cities were undeniably important. All places were. Married, divorced or single, people passed on: places remained. He was very happy that Edenmore would be remaining. The door of O'Sullivan's porch was open. He went in and chose the door to the left.

Mr O'Toole was alone, leaning on the counter, reading the *Daily Express* through spectacles which for some reason looked very odd on him.

'Well, my goodness,' he said, in his Cork lilt. ' 'Tis a long time since we've seen *you*, sorr.'

'Aye. And you look exactly the same, Mr O'Toole.'

The Major smiled, rather unnaturally.

'Me, is it? Oh, I'm afraid not. I have to wear these glasses now. First step to the grave. And did you not like the wedding?'

'Father Hanna is delivering a rather excessive oration.'

'Oh, of course. He's worse than a bishop.'

'Much worse. Won't you have a drop of the poison with me?'

'I never touch it. An Irish, is it?'

'Aye. It keeps the blood moving. I don't know how you manage.'

'Oh, I manage all right. And tell me now, sorr, is there to be another wedding? We hear talk of your daughter and this foreign gintleman.'

'I believe it's to be announced tonight. I don't know what's come over them all.'

'Well, I wouldn't know. I've managed without it, thank God. Your grandson was in a couple of months ago. I notice he didn't come back.'

'Really? He's returning to London.'

'I thought he would. 'Tis no place for him, among us *provincials*. He's a nice lad. Innocent, you know.'

'I suppose so.'

'You don't connect by asking questions. It takes longer than that.'

'Aye. A whole life for me would not be enough.'

'You see, in Ireland you're up against the slave mind. It's not our fault, God help us. We cannot meet a stranger except with flattery and every kind of falsehood. Keeping face, you know, the poor man's refuge.'

'It's a theory.'

'Oh, it's no theory, I assure you. And yet we like people, you know, if they have character. We like artists, for instance. Yes, more than film stars. Could you say that of England? Do you know who was here the other day? Harry C. Rodgers.'

'Oh!'

'An American. A novelist. He gave me his autograph. I have it above.'

'He didn't give you a book?'

'Ah, no, it's not the books so much. The man had character, because he was a writer and appreciated people. I've no doubt it's in his books, but only at second hand. We prefer people to print, you know.'

'It's not much help to their livelihood.'

'Oh, somebody buys them, I've no doubt. Oh, ho, what's all that now?'

Noises were heard from the road outside.

'I'd better show interest, I suppose. Many thanks, Mr O'Toole.'

'Not at all, sorr. Any time. We don't move.'

'Aye. I don't either.'

The whole congregation was out on the pavement, beside the row of cars, in a celebratory condition which the priest's address seemed to have done little to diminish. Kathleen and Trench stood at the centre of the crowd. Trench, with his grey underclothes buried deep under his immaculate façade, looked a splendid Edwardian figure, beaming with delight. Both were well covered with confetti and snow cast by the younger generation. Mary Cullen was even close to tears. So also, surprisingly, was Mrs Doyle. But all were given confidence by the extraordinary, radiant, transformed figure of Kathleen in her luxurious gown. Much moved, she impulsively rushed up to Grania and kissed her on the cheek. Seeing Moira standing near, she did the same to her. Then suddenly she took both by the hand, and looking at one, and then at the other, and losing her head completely, she exclaimed: 'My two mistresses!'

The party that was to be the talk of the capital for years began with a formidable operation by the Garda Siochána. A heavy cordon of police directed traffic and scrutinised arrivals at the gate of Edenmore. Large American taxis and other cars packed close to asphyxiation with the uninvited, came rolling out from Dublin over a period of several hours. A few practised performers, foreseeing difficulty, dismounted earlier and climbed the high wall, only to be apprehended by plain-clothes men within the grounds. Most, however, continued with a real sense of outrage on to the excavated car park and joined the night's flirtation at Cullen's in the most variegated costumes. Mr. Cullen, astounded by the resulting custom, formed the very best opinion of the Count, already rumoured to be paying for the reception, and was contemplating the removal of another of the green fields of Ireland to accommodate car owners and drinkers in case this occurred again.

Meanwhile, those in possession of the unusual invitation had been pouring into the brightly lit mansion, received by Grania dressed in a Grecian costume as patroness and Muse, with a cornucopia of Christmas crackers under one arm. In the long hall, with its fire, Christmas tree and chandeliers on high all glowing, they formed a brilliant assembly. On the landing Jimmy Griffin and his Four Aces, in newly laundered coats, holding back their livelier repertoire at Grania's request, played a soft accompaniment to the uproarious conversation of the guests meeting below. Among them, leading his white-coated team, each member being equipped with a silver tray of sparkling champagne, dancing ahead on mercurial feet, moved Flanagan, svelte and refreshed in a brown and green kilt. He had remembered Dermot's remark, and was delighted with the idea.

Possibly the most dramatic of all the arrivals was that of a bishop in full regalia, accompanied by Mephistopheles, in the back of a Buick. One member of the police, having said 'Good evening, Your Grace', and received a nod from Dermot, caught sight of the devil in the neighbouring seat, uttered a shout and a prayer, and had to be revived by his comrades. 'I told you we were overdoing it,' murmured Martin, nervously fingering the horns on his forehead.

Yet such was the crush that they only evoked a few gasps from those close at hand, among them Grania. Dermot was irritated.

'Who's that bint?' he said.

'Lady Tedesdale,' said Grania.

She was followed, at a distance, by Lord Tedesdale, who, although there was no marquee, had been taking the precaution of hiding his station wagon down the drive, among the rhododendrons.

'And who are all these gombeen-men?'

This would have taken a long time for Grania to answer.

From England there was a magnificent representation of near artists, most of them dressed in their usual clothes, because that was exactly how they fancied themselves. They were colourful. They included art editors of the 'glossies', scene and costume designers, television guitarists dressed like refined cowboys, fashion and free-lance photographers, foreign princes and princesses, all from Kensington, interior decorators, fashion editresses, several ladies-in-waiting, having an obvious holiday in the Republic, and some of the most important models in the country.

Mingling with this new English élite was the élite of the new Ireland: hand-weaving P.R.O.s, tweed and baneen couturiers, turf mould and Gaelic coffee publicity men, agents for folk song artists, contemporary pub designers, knitwear photographers and coarse fishing press officers.

Less successful, but cheerful as theatre people are, most of the

Abbey company was there in peasant costume, and most of the Gate in Restoration furbelows.

On the more intellectual side, Grania had provided some very long-established reviewers and several former angry young novelists changed overnight into plump literary critics. On the other hand, still unaltered by success, the enemy of compromise and one of the few who had accepted her challenge while completely misunderstanding it, the author of *The Kiss of Death* had come as The Bomb, a white casing constructed during overtime on the building lot, from which only his feet protruded. Contemptuous and impassioned, but physically deprived, as he now belatedly realised, of the ability to give expression to either emotion, he strode about in it, trusting that as many revellers as possible would be faced with the words painted thereon: 'And What About Tomorrow?'

Also in the literary category, Delia had arrived with Marc Albert Louvessin, Paulette Nin, Otto Kranz and Monika . . . in short the entire editorial staff of *A.* They were all in deep mourning for Arcoli, who had finally passed away, and they looked a melancholy and bewildered group, being concerned with the beginning and essence of all things and finding very few clues here. But Delia, as gipsy-haired though not as good-looking as her sister, was secretly relieved to be back where she could be herself, and not someone who is supposed to be on the Left Bank.

The 'county', with Lavinia Westmacott, Antoinette Haslipp and their diminished husbands, was not as well represented as the Major had hoped; although he asked himself whether his notions of something more interesting had any real basis.

There was also an obvious shortage of that most highly vaunted category, 'ordinary decent Dublin folk'; for which the Major, and everyone else, was heartily thankful.

Without exception the foreign guests were very soon engaged in abandonment, and even argument, that would have been inconceivable at home. There was something about this country that permitted long-denied speech and behaviour; a kind of unreality, so that they were confident that it would all be forgotten when they returned to the 'reality' of England. Although failing on the costumes, they were certainly being themselves; and it was a delight to visit such a place, though heaven help the people who had to live here. Abandonment was assisted by an abundance of champagne and by their new-found readiness to consume it in unusual quantity. Argument was assisted by the fact that Grania had given no consideration to possible embarrassments about which hostesses in the Home Counties might have been more careful; so that a dozen or so people had already tangled with previous partners, former intimates, and co-respondents still on the loose.

Two guests to which this danger might have applied in some degree found themselves free of it on meeting. Norah and Hugo greeted each other without constraint. Each was accompanied by a spouse, and on excellent terms. Norah wore the black off-the-shoulder ball-dress in which Terence Keogh had captured her. Veronica, in hidden delight at finding so many well-known people to take the lid off, was dressed, as ever, as a novelist renowned for her cutting edge; a grey sweater up to the neck, adorned with one row of pearls, and her hair combed back into a bun so that nothing would get in the way of her eagle eyes. Charlie wore his riding costume, while Hugo was dressed as Father Christmas. He had been appearing as such the previous night at a Christmas party for distressed newsvendors. Although the play was no longer running, and was awaiting a London theatre, Dublin had taken him to its heart at last, expressing its gratitude to an artist as only it knew how. In this same cause a native performer of great talent and forty years' service had eagerly accepted the same festive rig, and a cheque for two guineas, the previous Christmas. Hugo had almost at once noticed the bishop, knew that he should have been shocked, but really felt envious that he had not thought of it for himself.

Similarly the Major, in his riding kit, had spotted Charlie in his, and considered it an outrageous imposture.

Reggie Manningham was back from Jamaica, having returned to Hilda in sackcloth and ashes. The sackcloth was held round his waist by an old regimental tie, and some of the ashes had got into his hair. Since Hilda was dressed in her sack costume of brown Irish tweed, they made a perfect pair. Here again there was no constraint, because Dermot freely, and if the truth were told, with relief, raised his hand and gave his blessing to this brown couple. Reggie, with a red-veined face and military moustache, was not altogether surprised by Hilda's Celtic-Bohemian reversion, because she had once confessed to him that her mother, one of the Gloucestershire Truscotts, had in her youth broken with the family and posed as a Connemara peasant for Augustus John.

Moira had arrived, in much excitement, in her off-the-shoulder black ball-dress. Tom, who had been greatly taken with the challenge of presenting the true persona, and devoted hours to it, had settled on his farming coat and evening-dress trousers as being in his individual case the true gradation between the *via media* and the ultimate. But Moira had stopped it, saying he smelt too strongly of pig.

Meanwhile, up in Flanagan's quarters, the other party had been in progress for some hours, and yet the traditional fiddler, a man of eighty-three, was still playing with tireless energy, as was his elderly wife, who accompanied him by rattling and clashing a pair of tambourines. Mr O'Toole, hampered now and then by his cousin, Cornelius, was serving behind the temporary bar, while the Doyles and Trenches were stepping it out with a will, moving, turning and crossing over. Two of the ladies-in-waiting, with their escorts, having heard what they understood to be eightsome reels, had come up and been greeted by a wild character with 'Ye are welcome', and promptly taken to the floor; and thought it heaven. Mick Trench, on the other hand, had been pining for Jimmy Griffin and his Four Aces in the big house, but his new stepmother, now changed into her black dress with the red flowers, had forced him to dance and was triumphant. 'Give!'

she cried, neatly footing it in the traditional manner. 'Come on! Give!'

Among the non-dancers, the greatest surprise, and to some the greatest compliment, was the appearance of Father Hanna, who had come because he liked a drop and because he reasoned that if he had to warn his congregation about hell every Sunday he might as well know what it looked like. He was telling the bride's father a story he had heard from Father Conlan, and the old man's eyes were wide with amazement. He told it to show that he was human, although his arrival had shown this much better. Repeatedly, to his distress, he was approached by Julia Byrne, who had put away her Pioneer badge and taken one glass of champagne, and was full of congratulations and mysterious intimations. 'You told them, all right,' she said. 'You told them! But there's a lot more to be said. Two of my brothers are priests, and *I* should know. You've heard they're leaving, haven't you? Oh yes. Once they hear the cows mooin', they're off!'

Seated on one of the chairs, clapping her hands to the music, was the mountainous figure of Mr O'Toole's sister. Her dog with the bronchial trouble lay in her lap, and Kathleen was glad because it was company, even though of a rather sickly nature, for Richard. Mary Cullen, seated beside her, had for some time been talking about the gentry. She had decided that the Count very definitely belonged to that category, ever since he had stood at the kitchen door and clapped his hands together, and she had found herself leaving the roast, which she was basting in the oven, and going over to him as if hypnotised.

An hour or so later it was the Count who was to take a leading rôle in the night's performance. The Major was on the top landing when Grania appeared and said that they were about to make the announcement. He had been roaming his own house— or what used to be his own house—in a mood of growing exhaustion and irritation. Champagne had never agreed with him. He was suddenly opposed to these people and their farmyard motions; the chatter, the din, the desires, the worthless complications, the lack of peace, the lack of development and growth. He had wandered into his bedroom with some faint hope of retiring, and found, apparently, a wife and husband, and a former husband who was now her present lover, engaged in furious disputation.

'We're going to announce it now, Father," she said, excited and happy, with her cornucopia re-stocked with crackers. 'Are you coming downstairs?'

'Do you really think it's wise? You'll never manage him.'

'Oh, Father,' she said, genuinely hurt, 'support me for once, *please*. You yourself were impressed.'

'Not in your terms.'

'Pardon me.'

An American writer with large spectacles had joined them. 'I understand that you are our hostess tonight, madam?'

'Yes, yes.'

'You know, conformity is perhaps *the* major peril facing our society today. Certainly it is the major concern—indeed, I might almost term it the only concern—of our contemporary American authors. May I say, in honour bound, that it is fascinating, and truly admirable, that you should stage an actual, practical demonstration against it?'

'You may say anything if you keep it lively,' said Grania. 'Would you excuse us for a moment, please?'

'Certainly. Certainly.'

He bowed and moved away.

'You've wanted to mother them before,' said the Major. 'I suppose you know that he doesn't require it?'

'Doesn't he? How little you understand people, Father. Have you seen his panic when he gets a slight cold?'

'Pooh. Torture didn't worry him.'

'That's different. Come along now, Father. People are waiting.'

'Ah, yes, people.'

In the long hall the multitudes had already received an intimation that something unusual was about to happen. The dancing had been halted: Jimmy Griffin and the Aces had turned to their drinks. Flanagan and his staff had taken the crackers from the walls and distributed them among the company. The guests held them in expectation, and conversed even more volubly than before.

On meeting Charile again, Moira found that he was not so bad, and certainly not so good, as she had imagined. One could not overlook the fact that, in spite of his past behaviour, he was helping Tom to new heights with the multi-storied garage.

'That was a nice trick you tried on us!' she said.

'Ah, don't be too hard on me. It wasn't really my idea.'

'I believe we're going to hear who's come out top in that affair.'

'Yes,' he said. 'Our Polish friend. Good luck to him.'

'I'm happy for her. She deserves it.'

It was strange how detached she felt about him. Her dream was confirmed. Lately it had returned. Tom was again standing at the top of the stairs beside her, and from below, two by two, came Dublin. But no one approached to look at her with adoration, and when later she wandered upstairs and into the presence of the four-poster, it was empty.

Tom had met Patrick by the oak panelling and held him against it by the elbow, speaking confidentially.

'. . . a very remarkable occasion, and a very remarkable woman, your mother. She has given my wife and I a lesson in the liberal values, one must confess it. She has put us right, eh?'

'Yes. Ssh!'

Grania had asked Jimmy Griffin to produce a roll on the drums, and the room was falling silent.

'Take this Sleator fellow with whom I have just found myself in *conversazione.*' He gave Patrick an elbow equeeze. 'In ecclesiastical garb, mind you. A thing I would not previously have countenanced. A foul and obscene blasphemy, one might suppose, if you'll pardon my Greek. Yet I must confess that the man has a persona, and what's more appears to be a perfectly amiable fellow. The garb shows imagination. You can't get away from it.

Am I right? Give me the man that has imagination and I will wear him on my heart. . . . This is damn good champagne, Patrick, is it not?'

'Yes. Sssh.'

'What?'

The ballroom was now silent.

Grania stood on the stairs behind the Count, with the Major behind them.

'Ladies and gentlemen and members of the press, I will speak briefly,' said André, a resplendent bemedalled figure in extremely worn boots. 'I have proposed marriage, and I have been accepted. Naturally the lady of my choice is your unique hostess who stands beside me.'

There were cheers. Grania was embraced by the bishop, several near artists, and Father Christmas. 'Quite rightly, quite rightly!' roared André. The crackers were pulled and the hall was rent with explosions. Jimmy Griffin and the Aces were playing 'For He/She's a Jolly Good Fellow', led by a furiously gesticulating bishop. Paper hats had appeared everywhere, and tin whistles; and Flanagan had emerged from the kitchen with streamers which he flung at the guests with a fanciful arm motion but deadly accurate aim. The editorial staff of *A* was suddenly jubilant, in coloured headgear. Grania was plucking crackers from the cornucopia and hurling them into the company. Near artists of every kind had become even more relaxed than was the case before, and people of all sexes were embracing each other indiscriminately, while Hugo's Veronica hurried among them with the keenest eyes and the most retentive memory in contemporary fiction, and the flash-bulbs of both employed and free-lance photographers exploded like fireworks all over the room.

As the storm died and Jimmy Griffin and the Aces took over again, the dancers found themselves tripping and sliding over a mass of paper and streamers.

The Major watched them reflectively for some time: the Neelans and Gerratys and all the other couples, going round and round, parting for a time, mingling, and re-forming again.

Patrick and Ann did not separate. He was much too happy with his partner, and content now with the Anglo-Irish compromise: he could easily come back here, drink at the well of individualism and escape again, when satiated, to the comfort of anonymous activity. As the Major had guessed, Ann, too, was going to London.

Norah was with Charlie, who was certainly the best dancer in the room. 'I knew we'd seen the Count somewhere before,' she said. 'In France. It's strange. I'd forgotten all about France.' Why had she ever yearned for foreign parts? Everything was here. As if tonight was not enough, a few moments ago she had been listening to a group of actors talking about a pre-London production opening after Christmas, called *The Taste of Cyanide,* which sounded much more cheerful than Hugo's play, and was starring the handsome Harry Newbolt, whom she would very much like to meet.

While Moira danced with Lawrence Hurley, Tom went jigging around the floor with his dumpy wife. It was extraordinary. She had seen Lawrence around Dublin for years and years, and he was dressed now exactly as he had been in the gallery that afternoon. Yet he was different, somehow. She had never before noticed quite how attractive he was, and she had certainly not been aware that he was such a marvellous dancer.

The Major was approached by the bishop, who said: 'Where the — hell has that O'Keeffe got to? I've met a moron who thinks he's an art critic.'

'I'm afraid I don't know.'

Martin had stepped out into the yard at the rear, to reflect in the silence there. He had already met the same editor, of a London journal, who thought that there were decided possibilities of employment. The reception in Flanagan's rooms had finally expired with the departure of bride and groom, and there were no lights on across the yard. Nor was there a moon. But all the stars were out. He stood gazing at them in the Mesphistophelian horns which Dermot had termed an unconscious representation of the 'long horns' that were allegedly on 'the cows across the water'.

The same stars were shining over London, he thought.

Noises were coming from above, but he paid no attention. An excited and enthusiastic group was unloading the Bomb through one of the upper windows. There were murmurs of 'Easy there!' and 'Over to your right a bit,' and suddenly it was released. There was a whistling sound in the darkness and it landed with a thud and a muffled cry, on the thick snow of the yard. Martin took no notice.

'Oh, London, London!' he reflected.

At the same time the Major, with his own particular desire for peace, had slipped out through the front door, and stood on the steps. The light was on the distant gate-lodge, and he saw two people, who he had no doubt were Paddy and Finola, moving in the rhododendrons.

If his grandson married this girl, he thought, they might produce children. That would be nice. The house was devoid of children, and adults were on the whole terrible.

Faintly behind him, through the heavy door, he could hear the music, and Jimmy Griffin singing:

'I'm dreaming of a white Christmas,
Just like the ones we used to know . . .'

People going and people staying; pairings and marriages; and occasionally people nudging each other into new directions. The familiar cycle. Let the young travel, and let those capable of it make the real journey.

The night was very cold, and the stars remarkable. Nature had its familiar cycle too. He looked at the dimly visible white lawn, and wished to goodness it would hurry up. He wanted the thaw. He was anxious to get down to some serious weeding.

Mrs Kathleen Trench, who was also not going anywhere, opened the door of the gate-lodge. She was allowing her husband—just this once—to make her a cup of tea. No sound of the music was audible from there. She emerged on the stone step and stood in the profound silence, gazing at the panoply of stars, and thought for a moment that she might burst.

Then, because there was no one to observe or rebuke her, because she was out of uniform and mistress of her own home, she commenced, slowly at first, to click her fingers and stamp her feet. Meanwhile, with a languorous motion, she had been pushing out her bottom, and now, as she increased the tempo of the clicking fingers to a sound like rapid gunfire, she began suddenly to jerk it up and down in as exact an imitation as she could contrive of the Spanish dancers she had seen that night at the Olympia; when Finola, for some reason which was now never likely to be explained, had suffered from hiccoughs throughout the whole of the second half.